Scientists:

*Their Psychological
World*

Scientists:

Their Psychological World

B E R N I C E T.

E I D U S O N

Foreword by Harrison Brown

Basic Books, Inc. · *Publishers*
N E W Y O R K

© 1962 by Basic Books Publishing Co., Inc.

Library of Congress Catalog Card Number: 61-15725

Printed in the United States of America

Book design by Guy Fleming

FOREWORD
by
HARRISON BROWN

WHETHER WE LIKE IT OR NOT (AND
many persons don't) we are living in a world in which
science and technology largely determine the ways in which
we live and die. Several thousand years ago, following the
revolutionary discoveries that man could cultivate crops and
domesticate animals, we became dependent for our survival
upon the farmer and the herdsman. The situation in which
we find ourselves today is analogous; however, our dependence
has been transferred from the farmer and the herdsman to
the scientist and the engineer. During the last half-century
we have seen the power and influence of the farmer dwindle,
and we have seen an upsurge in the influence of people who
are technically trained. Without such persons the enormous
complex of mines, factories, transportation and communication systems (which is the heart of modern civilization) would
not function for long. The military establishment would

wither. Even the farmer and the herdsman have become dependent upon the smooth functioning of technology.

A symptom of our heightened dependence upon technology is the dramatic increase in the number of scientists and engineers involved in government at high level. Barring a major war, this is an irreversible trend. In view of this fact, it is important that we inquire into the natures of these persons. What are they like? What motivates them? How do they react to specific situations? What is their outlook upon life and society?

An examination of the nature of technically trained people is all the more important because they represent such a small, although increasing proportion of the citizenry in relation to their influence and importance. At one time the farmers, who filled the greater part of the human subsistence requirements, made up most of the population. Today, their replacements, the scientists and engineers, number but 1 per 200 of the population and it is difficult to imagine that they will ever exceed two per cent. Being such a small group, it is quite easy for the general public to have distorted views of the scientist and his nature.

Bound as society is to the scientist and the engineer, it is of increasing importance that technical people be understood by the population generally. This is not only because the influence of such persons is spreading. An equally important consideration is that as the years pass our society will need increasing numbers of them. It is important that we recognize embryo scientists and engineers early; it is important that they be educated in such a way that society will benefit to the greatest possible extent.

Bernice Eiduson's study of the psychology of scientists is, I believe, a significant addition to the literature on this subject. I have read it with great interest and believe that it will be useful to the educator, stimulating to the scientist, and highly illuminating to the thinking public.

PREFACE

I CAME TO THE STUDY OF RESEARCH scientists via a study of artists. For many years I had worked as a clinical psychologist in a psychiatric clinic whose patient load was heavily sprinkled with writers, artists, musicians, actors—persons who had sought out creative fields as their life work. These people sought psychiatric help for a number of personal reasons—marital difficulties, somatic illnesses, depression, sexual problems, phobias, and work difficulties. As I became familiar, through professional contacts, with the kinds of psychological demands that creative fields make on the persons in them, I became interested in these artists as a group. It seemed to me that only a specific type of personality could go into work that valued such characteristics as originality and talent; that required perseverance and inner strength in the face of neglect, disinterest, and misunderstanding. The art fields as vocations seemed to me to produce more anxiety and tensions than satisfactions. I therefore decided to undertake a study of the personality structure of the persons in the arts.

As these artists were seen in diagnostic study (they were interviewed about their social history, examined psychiatrically, tested with a battery of psychological tests) and particularly when they were seen more intensively if taken into psychiatric treatment, it became evident that many of the descriptions or theoretical formulations about the personality of the creative person that appeared in psychological and psychiatric literature were incorrect. Systematic study of the hypotheses about artists showed that many notions were inconsistent and contradicted each other, that the literature was filled with vague and esoteric explanations about how creativity came about and what a creative person was really like. It was apparent too that most of the formulations had been based on studies of artists who were long dead, and that at best a lot of "psychological archeology" was being practiced, with life histories and biographical information carefully but often fancifully reconstructed. It seemed to me therefore very important to sort out speculations and hypotheses about artists that were correct and that could be empirically validated from those that were incorrect. I thought it high time we knew whether artists were indeed different from men and women who chose fields that did not primarily require creative talents. I thought it important to see whether there were any features in the way artists thought or perceived problems, any commonnesses in personality structure and motivation which all artists shared and which thus would permit us to identify and distinguish them as a group.

Since obviously a group of persons in the arts who have come to a psychiatric clinic for personal help might be labeled neurotic, I did not want to use a patient group as the only subjects from whom to draw conclusions about the personality of artists. I was afraid too that using patients as subjects might unwittingly reinforce the old stereotype that neurosis was a necessary ingredient for creative endeavor. To overcome this difficulty I drew upon a second group of artists, comparable to the first group in age, sex, intelligence, formal education, and areas of work chosen. None of this group had sought any psychiatric help, nor did individual personal history or personality picture show any grossly pathological features. As a third step I selected as another control group persons who had selected fields of business—sales, accounting, corporate management—and decided to subject them to the same clinical experimental procedures which would be administered to the artists. I thought that this would permit me to test whether persons in the arts revealed characteristics different from those that defined persons in another vocational field. I chose individuals in business for this third group not because work in business is necessarily uncreative; the growth and development of American industry would certainly attest to the inventiveness and creativity there. But the business fields, unlike the creative fields of the arts, do not state that originality and creative talent are the most highly prized and valued characteristics—the *sine qua non* for making any mark at all.

Subsequently I subjected all these groups to psychological study—which consisted of projective tests and intensive clinical interviews about themselves, their early development, their personal history. All the test data were then turned over to judges who knew nothing about the nature of the study. They were merely asked to rate all the subjects, using the information which the test data provided them, on a rating scale which was based on the hypotheses that repeatedly cropped up in the literature on the creative person, his emotional and personal behavior, the ways he thought, and the motivations that stimulated and directed his behavior.

This study successfully differentiated the persons in the arts from the persons in the fields of business. (It incidentally also struck a death blow at the old "neurotic artist" theme—the "wound and arrow" theme about which Edmund Wilson and Lionel Trilling have debated—for the investigation showed that the neurotic features in the group of artists who sought psychiatric help were not those bound up in the characteristics that identified them as creative persons.)

Simply because the variables identifying the artist from the nonartist appeared to be so clear cut, the next logical question was whether these same characteristics applied only to persons who had sought work in the fields of the arts, or whether they cut across single vocational fields and could be said to characterize persons in other creative fields—the sciences, for example. If this were borne out, then it might be said that such traits identified all persons who go into creative fields, irrespective of the particular work. As a next step, therefore, I asked a group of research scientists, all men working in the fields of the natural sciences in university or academic installations, to participate in the same experimental procedures that had been administered to the artists and to the businessmen. Forty scientists agreed; thus, the present study.

Although I have limited this book to an elaboration of the quantitative and qualitative findings on the research scientist, the findings about them were derived by comparing them as a group to the artists and to the businessmen. I have put some of the statistical data on all of the three groups in Appedix II, so that persons who are interested in seeing some of the statistical analyses on which the study was based can look at the raw materials. However, although this book treats only of the research scientists, its implications seem to me to rest also in what it tells us about the person who goes into any field of creative endeavor, for on the basis of the clinical experimental data both artists and scientists seem to share the same ways of thinking about and perceiving problems and situations; seem to share many attitudes about what they do, respond to the same motivations, and display some of the same personality attributes. The experimental findings showed that artists and scientists were more alike in their cognitive characteristics than they were in personality features, but in both of these areas the persons who were in creative fields were significantly different from persons who had selected business vocations. Therefore, I feel that this material speaks for a general model of the person who goes into a creative vocation, a model which stems in large part from the characteristics displayed in mental functioning and to a lesser degree from the psychodynamics and motivational structure of the individual.

My decision to limit this book to the findings on the research scientists came from the response to the study as it became known and reported in part in professional publications. The scientists themselves were interested in and introspective about their creative activities. This seemed to me to be a rather recent development. Some years ago Lawrence Kubie had written two articles in the *American Scientist* (1953, 1954) in which he had pointed out how much the psychology of the research scientist affected his efficiency as a scientist, his choice of problems, his decision about the lines of research to pursue, his subsequent attacks on the problems, and his ambitions for himself. Kubie was pointing out that the usual, normal, nonpathological everyday activities of the scientists, like all other areas of his life, reflect the general way he handles situations, the way he chooses stimuli to which to respond, his general attitudes, and his interests and personal psychodynamics. Kubie's material was based on the psychoanalysis of scientists who had been sufficiently disturbed by personal problems either at home or at work to have sought professional help; and because of this data source, many scientists to whom I spoke had the notion that the insights he profferred were appropriate only when personal psychological motivations invaded work too much or were not sufficiently fended off from the normal flow of activity. In other words, they were appropriate only to the disturbed scientist, and since few scientists wanted to feel that they were disturbed, the Kubie articles made little dent on the scientific community. Had they first appeared today or even a few years ago, I think they would have met a different reception. The scientists themselves seem to be more comfortable today in actively thinking about their own ways of work. The pressure for achievement and accomplishment created by outside events has demanded this. Scientists have an urgent need to stimulate the young people around them, particularly those who work in settings where they see students of unmistakable talent who are not sufficiently disciplined to carry through a Ph.D. program or a piece of postgraduate research to the point of completion; and they have begun to look at these students in terms of what their own experiences and knowledge can contribute to their understanding of them. Also, the scientist's self-consciousness about his "mental health" status is abated because this facet of his personality is becoming less and less a part of the stereotype about him. Although some recent studies still report that high school and college students think of scientists as "strange, erratic, or odd-ball," the scientific image has expanded to include many other personality facets. Colleagues who misuse or waste time and ability are beginning to arouse some compassion and some anxieties in researchers themselves. Furthermore, the spate of speeches and articles on the responsibility and obligations of scientists to society, to this world, and the worlds to come has contributed to the scientist's willingness to examine himself.

As I learned how involved scientists are in these psychological problems, I decided to limit the material to be included in this book to the data about the research scientist alone. Some of these data have been presented at meetings of physiologists, experimental biologists, and in *Science*, as well as at psychological meetings, and the response of research scientists themselves has made me feel that at this time when they are reaching out for information about themselves it would be appropriate to summarize my data, to try at least in part to fill their needs. I have tried to look at the material from many angles, and I have leaned heavily on their exact quotations.

I planned the study and gathered the interview and test data on the research scientists when I was Research Psychologist for the Hacker Foundation for Psychiatric Research and Education, Beverly Hills, California. This Foundation, therefore, supported that aspect of the study. As the investigation progressed and showed promise of being a worthwhile piece of work, I applied for funds to the customary governmental and nongovernmental agencies and foundations that frequently support research in the fields of scientific creativity. However, I had no success in getting funds, and I felt that I was running into an overly cautious attitude on the part of such groups toward giving monies to private foundations, or to clinics devoted primarily to service-oriented work, or to individuals not formally affiliated with universities. It was my good fortune to have a research scientist, a biochemist, as husband, and because of his interest in this investigation, as well as in the investigator, he supported both through the stages that are reported here. Needless to say, he was not one of the subjects.

A number of friends and colleagues were helpful in reading and criticizing the manuscript. I want to single out Drs. Malcolm S. MacLean of the Department of Education at UCLA, Frederick J. Hacker of the Hacker Foundation for Psychiatric Research and Education, and Edwin Shneidman of the Veterans Administration Center in Los Angeles, whose comments were particularly incisive. Regretfully, the subjects themselves must remain nameless. I can only record their friendliness, their ready contribution of time and effort and their genuine enthusiasm for the project. Their willingness to expose themselves to study seemed to me exemplary of the highest kind of scientific morality.

BERNICE T. EIDUSON

May 1961
Los Angeles

CONTENTS

Scientists:

Their Psychological World

I

The Men and the Study

THIS BOOK GREW OUT OF WHAT I thought was a curious paradox: that men of science, who search for truth, who try to show things as they really are, to separate fact from fiction, to strip rationalization from reality, have themselves become shrouded in so much mystery and myth in the public mind.

The images, or stereotypes, of the scientist are various, and they can be traced to several sources, each interpreting and presenting scientists from a different point of view: the biographers, who have tried to describe them as human figures, usually heroic in proportion; the historians, who have attempted to understand them as products of their times; the psychologists, who have ferreted out what information they could about the personality of great scientists *a poste-*

riori and dutifully pasted these bits of information together in a preset psychological collage.

We have been left with some peculiar and contradictory pictures of what scientists are like. One stereotype, for instance, portrays the scientist as a "pure" seeker of truth—pure either in the sense that he is relatively independent of his general environment, or in the sense that he is free from such "impure" motives as material gain or the wish to please an employer. Another stereotype envisions him as an unruly, irresponsible child, who nevertheless remains loved, admired, or envied because of his great talent. A part of this stereotype is the notion that the scientist is a neurotic or psychotic of a special order, whose disturbance has to be accepted, even praised, because it forms a part of his creativeness. Still another stereotype, offered by those who adhere to the "inspiration" or "Eureka!" theory of creativity, describes scientists as persons "chosen to receive experiences which haphazardly strike these select few with flashes of inspiration."

All these theories picture scientific creativity as somehow "innate," arising from peculiar, inherent abilities which find expression either without any assistance from environmental circumstances or with just the right sociopsychological push. In this view, scientists and their work live in a separate world, removed from the laws of the social and cultural milieu in which they happen to be placed. Even success, or accomplishments, must be judged in other terms —not by conventional standards, but by special mores appropriate only to scientists. The result of this attitude has been to stamp the scientist as a person apart, indifferent to ordinary rewards, and unmindful of what preoccupies lesser men.

Just now, to add to the confusion, an energetic effort has been made to change the public image of the scientist to exactly the opposite of the foregoing: to picture him as a common man, a human man who could and should be emulated by every American child. This switch may stem in part from what some see as a general tendency toward leveling or averaging in a democratic society, and a consequent attempt to deny that excellence or creativity can exist as an observable phenomenon. Others see the switch as a propaganda measure fostered deliberately to overcome antipathy to science and to lure more children into scientific careers. In any case, to the scientist, who has been more symbol than man, and who has become accustomed to be regarded as something of an oddity, this change in propaganda about himself is an astonishing turn of affairs.

Nevertheless, there is some evidence that this new approach has already modified the earlier notions, judging from some of the recent studies of attitudes. One such study found the researcher described as a highly intelligent man, devoted to his work at the expense of interest in art, friends, and even family. He was described further as:

A person who gets great personal satisfactions, sense of success, reasonably high status in the community, and a modest income from his work. He serves mankind in a selfless way, almost unaware he is doing so, and at the same time serves others by serving himself. In public affairs he is influential but maybe somewhat naïve. He is extreme in his views on social matters and tends to become emotionally involved with issues outside the realm of his professional competence. He is coldly intellectual in his work but excitable in the public political sphere. He is an "egghead" but not withdrawn like colleagues in the humanities; rather he is vigorously directed in the use of his intelligence. Therefore he turns out to be a strange, somewhat contradictory man who is hard to comprehend.[1]

Here it becomes apparent, that some of the former images of the scientist are being rephrased into psychological terms which are frequently used to describe persons in general, thus implying a beginning awareness that scientists may share with other people some personality features and motivations. However, the descriptions do not add up to a consistent whole, nor do they end up with a picture that is sufficiently fused with pleasant or appealing qualities for young people. In the Mead and Metraux study of high school students, which produced a composite of the scientist that was very similar to that held by the college students, the boys said they did not want to become scientists themselves, and the girls did not want to marry scientists. They seemed to feel that the scientist's orientation was antithetical to their values and they sensed a gap between his motivations and theirs, which they blamed on the wide discrepancy between what the scientist knows and does and thinks about, and what they do.

Striking also in these studies is how rapidly scientists' personalities become depicted in highly patterned and stereotypic ways, even if an old image shifts to something a little more appropriate. Even those "human characteristics" with which he is now identified have become so pat and overgeneralized that they allow for no diversity among scientific men. This is not merely a function of the inexperienced or immature student, or of an uninformed public, for faculty members at one university described the science faculty with whom they worked in the same stereotypic ways that the students had, a finding which incidentally might have been predicted from Holton's analysis of the projections about science and scientists which have created antipathy toward them in other intellectuals.[2]

One other current development seems also to be contributing to the tendency to portray the scientist in stereotype—his recent recognition by American humorists. In the last few years he has become a frequent subject of caricature, as had the psychiatrist before him. Laboratories, wind chambers, and interchanges between scientists are now often the scenes and the butt of jokes and cartoons. Although such portrayal would seem to imply ridicule and condemnation, we know from studies done on the significance of caricatures about psychiatrists, that these actually mean that public interest in the field is high.[3] As F. Redlich has pointed out, "At one time the midwife was the target of caricature; now her influence is so insignificant that the attack is unwarranted." Furthermore, if the psychodynamic meaning of caricature holds for the scientist as it does for the psychiatrist, the increasing number of cartoons should be welcome. It should mean that the scientist is experiencing a high degree of public status, respect, and authority, and that society is trying to defend itself against the anxieties that obvious weaknesses in this authority create by invoking the sharp weapon of caricature. Caricature, however, capitalizes upon stereotypes and in so doing, unfortunately entrenches these stereotypes more deeply than ever.

In the light of this prevailing tendency to think of the scientist exclusively in stereotype, it seemed to me that an empirical study of living men currently in research science was long overdue. It was essential to know which of the varied stereotyped conceptions were correct and which were not; and whether scientists could accurately be thought of as a "type." This kind of investigation had been previously stymied because of some of the images about the scientists as creative and creative persons that I mentioned above. The "inspirational" and mystical hypotheses had supported the idea that the origin and nature of the scientist's creative mental processes were unknown, that separation and uniqueness were somehow essential ingredients of his creative productivity, and that all attempts to study creativity intimately would run the risk of destroying the very thing that they set out to investigate.

My clinical experience in working with persons in

7

creative fields had persuaded me that this attitude might be unduly cautious,[4] and so I decided to undertake a study of creative scientists. I wanted to see what the research scientist was like as a person, whether his functioning could be understood in terms of our present theories of personality, or whether, as the images suggested, he eluded or defied the customary concepts of motivation. I wanted to know if there was such a thing as a "scientific personality," if scientists could be identified by means other than the ideas they deal with, the instruments they use, or the skills they have developed. I wondered what personal resources, mechanisms, and facilities lure men into professions that demand originality and individuality and then permit them to continue in and enjoy work which often produces tension and anxiety. Finally, I wanted to find out which of the many notions about scientists would actually stand up to analysis and experimental test.

I therefore asked forty research scientists to submit to psychological study. I did not select the group randomly, nor do they represent, in a specifically experimental sense, an average group. No particular conscious bias of status, specialty, or manner of work color the selections; I consider the group heterogeneous in all respects except the one on which the selection was based, choice of profession. In this way, I hoped to encourage individual characteristics to emerge, to allow fullest play to the variations rather than to the similarities.[5]

This basis of selection, resting solely on the criterion of choice of profession and its pursuit in an academic and research-oriented atmosphere, sounds arbitrary and narrow. Yet it is in line with my assumption that all of these men have been drawn into research work, not by accident or impulse, but because certain psychological features in their personality structures are expressed in their vocational choice. The factors that determine occupational choice seem

8

o me analogous to the factors that determine the other per-
onal choices an individual makes during his lifetime; thus,
he selection of one's work becomes significant for the under-
tanding of certain facets of behavior.[6]

All the men in the sample are male Caucasians, ranging
n age from 28 to 65, the mean being 41.7 years. They are
ll affiliated with a university or an academic installation on
he West Coast. Some devote themselves completely to re-
earch, doing all of the experimental or theoretical work
hemselves; others direct the research of students, fellows,
nd assistants. Some teach, and most engage in some ad-
ninistrative duties, but they all consider themselves primar-
ly research scientists. Six of the scientists work in physics,
ix in earth and soil sciences, twelve in chemistry, and six-
een in the biological and zoological sciences. They have
een in science for an average of fifteen years beyond the
h.D. degree. In academic rank the sample ranges from
fteen full professors to five assistant professors. The most
rolific of the researchers has produced over two hundred
cientific books and articles; the least, three.

I have deliberately avoided using success as a criterion
n the study because I feel that the motivations and personal
lynamics that lead to choice of scientific work are very much
he same for the successful man as for the unrecognized.
What success means in science is difficult to establish; it is
s dependent upon almost as many sociological variables as
s the establishment of artistic success.

If we use the yardstick of "reputation," this group is
mpressive. Each man holds at least the Ph.D. degree, and ex-
ensive memberships in his respective professional and scien-
ific societies. Almost half have been nominated to the Na-
ional Academy of Sciences in this country and many are
nembers of academies in foreign countries. Sixteen of the
nen have been awarded scientific honors—prizes, awards,
nedals of distinction, and honorary doctorate degrees—and

two have received the Nobel Prize. Along with the world famous, there are men whose careers have been long and dedicated, who have made consistent, but not striking, research contributions, whose work may live more through the men they have influenced than through their own discoveries. The group includes, as well, men whose achievements are still in embryo and fantasy.

I have looked at these research scientists from five different vantage points: I examined first their developmental histories and personal backgrounds in order to see what, if any, early experiences and relationships were common to the group. I was concerned with impressions of their parents, what their parents' occupations were, and how parental attitudes about work might have affected their sons' feelings about education and achievement. I wondered whether the intellectual endowment of the men had been recognized early, and, if so, what role this recognition played in suggesting adult work choice; and I looked for any particular experiences that might be considered consistently predisposing to scientific inquiry.

The second area of investigation was the adult personality structure of the scientists, their emotional behavior patterns and their motivations—particularly those surrounding work. In this area I was interested in the answers to such questions as: Are there any personality traits found with significant regularity among scientists? For example, are they particularly withdrawn or passive, or given to mood swings? Are they prone to particular kinds of conflicts or anxieties that contributed to their original choice of vocation or that have been aroused through their work? Do they have particular ways of handling anxieties, insecurities, tensions? Are they particularly responsive to certain drives and needs that get expressed in work? Do they show unusual reactions to stress? What are their aspirations and goals, and how do these compare with their potential?

A third focus of study is related to how the scientists, as a group, think and perceive—in other words, their styles of thinking. Here I was interested in how the scientists' intellectual capacities are expressed, whether their thinking is marked by originality and unusual flexibility—the intellectual traits frequently described as typical of creative people. I wondered if they were unusually sensitive to external stimuli and whether they showed highly developed abstracting ability and excellent integrative capacities. I wondered also whether experimentalists showed the same cognitive patterns as did theoreticians.

Two additional objects of the study turn toward the sociopsychological area, focussing on the individual scientist in relation to his group. For the situation of the scientist within the scientific community, I looked at those self-images of research scientists that reflect their identities as members of this profession, the ties that bind them to each other and suggest their continuing patterns of action and reaction and that allow outsiders to see them as a single and in some respects uniform body of men. The notions they hold about themselves were compared with their ideas about what scientists ideally should be, and I examined the compromises in function and philosophy that have emerged through their membership in a scientific world in which certain practices and ethics have been established and certain values extolled. Finally, I turned to the nonscientific aspects of the man—the part he plays in family life, as a member of a community, his patterns of work and play.

The psychologist has two general approaches to the individual—the statistical (or the actuarial) and the clinical.

With the first technique, one may classify an individual on the basis of objective information obtained from his life history, from subjective interview impressions, or from psychological test scores. These data can be combined to categorize a person, and once such classification is made, sta-

tistical tables can give the frequencies of various behavior
for persons in this grouping. The results, which are usuall
expressed in probability figures, in the end describe, not the
individual, but rather a hypothetical man. For some, thi
empirically determined statistical frame will give a fairly ac
curate fit; for others, scarcely a fit at all. As Ben Shahn ha
put it, "The statistical approach approximates everyone and
resembles no one."

Certainly, in describing the motivations and activities
the eccentricities and peculiarities of the individual, the
impersonality of statistical data seems to obliterate unique
ness and individuality. This is the point at which some psy
chologists have turned to the clinical method. In this in
dividually oriented approach, the psychologist again gather
historical information, personal impressions in interviews
and psychological test materials. However, these data are no
classified; instead, the investigator uses them as the basis fo
psychological hypotheses about the structure and dynamic
of a particular individual. Then, taking into account certain
reasonable expectations about outside events, predictions ar
made about the individual's behavior. To date, it has been
difficult to translate some of these data into established cate
gories that can be treated statistically, and one of the mos
active questions in psychology is whether the two approache
are reducible to each other, or whether they do in fact pic
up qualitatively different aspects of behavior which represen
different human phenomena.

In this study my techniques of investigation involv
both approaches, for I first do a comparative study on th
forty researchers in order to elicit the common denominato
in the various aspects of personality and behavior studied
and then I treat these data as if this were a case study of
single individual and I try to understand the role thes
variables play in the functioning of the scientist and in hi
psychological makeup. The raw data of the study wer

12

provided by administering two psychological tests to each scientist, and then interviewing them in open-ended, depth interviews. The tests, the Rorschach Test of Personality Diagnosis, and the Murray Thematic Apperception Test, are among the most widely used diagnostic instruments, and consist of ambiguous visual stimuli to which the subject responds by saying what comes to his mind when he is confronted with them. They have been frequently described as tests of creative imagination, or as methods of stimulating fantasy which encourage the expression of conscious and unconscious motives, impulses, conflicts, and defenses. The theory of projective testing rests on the assumption that the individual organizes experience as he twists, shapes, fits, and distorts people and situations into the framework of what Lawrence Frank has called "his private world." The test stimuli are purposely vague, ambiguous, plastic or manipulable so that a subject must impose his structuring or organizing principles on them in order to respond. In this way the projective instruments evoke from the subject his characteristic ways of investing situations with meaning, especially emotional meaning, and of giving them values and significance. In so doing, he reveals various aspects of his personality processes, and we are able to discover the relationship between these dynamic processes and his observable speech, feelings and attitudes.[7]

More specifically, the Rorschach Test presents a series of ink blots to which the subject responds by telling what the blot looks like, what it suggests, or of what it reminds him. Not only what an individual sees in the way of content but also the ways he sees and describes his images, when he sees them, and why, and how each individual response fits into the over-all configuration of the responses he produces are significant. The Rorschach Test is very revealing of the individual's strategies of defense and modes of adaptation, of his stabilities and his pathologies, of his conscious and un-

13

conscious values, wishes, aspirations, of his threats, anxieties, and guilts, and of what has been called the "over-all color and tone" of his personality.

The Thematic Apperception Test, more structured and less ambiguous, involves a series of magazine-like pictures of one or more persons in various poses and situations. The respondents elaborate the past and the future, as well as describing the present. In scoring and interpreting the TAT, the thread of the stories created is taken into account, as are such aspects as the popularity or origimlity of themes, whether certain stimuli are ignored or rejected, the kinds of persons who are consistently fashioned into heroes and into villains, the persons excluded, the situations that provoke conflictual imagery. This test suggests not only the conscious and unconscious identifications of the subject but also the play of his emotional reactions, such as dominance and dependency, generosity and possessiveness, wrath, and other personality dimensions.

The test data were submitted to three judges who were acquainted neither with the nature of the study nor with the sample under scrutiny. They were female, had the Ph.D. in psychology, and are experienced clinicians. They were instructed to examine the two tests together and rate them according to assigned variables which had to do with the scientists' characteristics of thinking and perceiving, their personality structures and emotional pictures, the kinds of motivation to which they respond—variables culled from the literature on the creative person in general, and the scientist in particular. These are listed in Appendix I.

The interviews were informal, made up mainly of open-ended questions, and dealt with the personal and developmental history of the men, their family backgrounds, their growing-up years, their present life styles. They were tape recorded in from one to three sessions which lasted from one and a half to three hours each. In those talks I was

14

interested in their evaluation of their capacities, their interests; in their view of the world around them; in their present attitudes toward science and toward other intellectual pursuits; in the kinds of people, situations, and things that they remembered as being important to them in childhood; in their conflicts, their struggles, and their satisfactions. I tried, in these interviews, to look at these men in terms of the ways that, to use Gardner Murphy's phrase, they have "invested" themselves psychologically, the ways they have, as individuals, focussed upon preferences and likings for certain things and rejected others, and ultimately developed a consistently used set of activities and objects to satisfy their drives and their needs. I was interested too, in their ideas about creativity and the creative process, and in their ways of judging creativity in students. I found the scientists for the most part outwardly friendly, generous with their time, and entrusting of their intimate personal histories. Many said that they had enjoyed participating in this study and had agreed to take part because they felt some responsibility toward furthering the investigation of scientific creativity. Some preferred the interviews over the psychological tests, although few were completely naïve about these instruments. Some were candid about the anxiety and tension that the whole process created in them; some were diffident; others became defensive. When a few gave vent to their fantasies about the results, they belabored the behavioral sciences.

I was especially interested to see how some of the scientists perceived colleagues who had been earlier subjects of the study, and I tried to include some of these "cross-references" when I thought them effective in showing how the images scientists have about others reflect their own self-concepts.

I studied the interviews with many precautions in mind. As might have been expected, some of the respondents attributed the routes their scientific careers have taken to specific determinants and circumstances, whereas others cited many factors. Some were confident that they were aware of all their motivations, others were more cautious, and still others defended their feeling that their choice had no rational or explicable basis. As often as possible I have presented the interview data verbatim. In some instances, the verbal data and the test material data seem different. As a clinical psychologist, I am confident that the tests are less open to conscious distortion and are thus probably more representative of some of the unconscious factors determining behavior; that the projective tools expose some of the rationalizations and distortions which tend to become major sources of error in interviews.[8]

In psychology, attempts to establish direct indices of relationships between any single factor and an apparent result are, at best, tentative and can often be misleading. Clinical psychologists have been careful to point out that isolating single characteristics can alter their significance. In examining any phenomenon of human behavior, a cause and-effect relationship which is obvious may not be particularly significant, whereas a subtle relationship which must be "teased out" of the data can in the long run prove the meaningful one.

We can study single, isolated aspects of an individual's behavior from a number of different viewpoints. In classical psychology interest has centered on these isolated phenomena in relation to pathology or personality disorder, for we have been alerted to the diseased aspects of functioning evidenced through psychological symptom formation or behavioral malfunction. This orientation has historical precedence in psychology, where the study of the abnormal provided our first insights into the normal and shaped our first conceptions of the individual. Man had been seen as a compromising and defensive organism who has had to adapt his in stinctual longings or primitive drives to the demands of the social world. Recently, however, behavioral scientists have become aware of how many human processes are not adequately accounted for in such a conception of personality—the searching, developing, manipulative aspects, for example, which are put to use not exclusively in defense or compromise but rather in the service of synthesizing, exploring, discriminating, and making use of the environment in satisfying and gratifying ways.

Psychologists have seen that what appears at first glance to be a disturbance may, at one and the same time or at different times and in different situations, be a strength- and stability-giving mechanism, a tension-binding device that in fact facilitates personality function and development. This is not so arbitrary nor paradoxical as it sounds; it reflects, rather, the current feeling that an absolute judgment of good or bad, of valuable or deleterious cannot be made about any particular aspect of behavior without taking into account its use in the over-all functioning of the personality. Psychologists have recognized that the separation between the negative defenses and backward strivings of the individual, and the so-called positive, creative, forward-looking urges, is an artificial one, more suitable to classification than to actual description. Clinical and experimental observation indicate that behavior is an apparent mixture and fusion of experiences proceeding simultaneously in many directions, and that many experiences are so indefinite and ambiguous that they are, at one and the same time, frustrating and gratifying, facilitating and hindering, and defensive and developmental.[9]

Thus, when the sociopsychological history of the scientists is regarded with an experimental approach, we can find, in equal measure, pathologies and fixations pointing to potential maladjustment, and creative, individually fulfilling, and adjustive experiences. It is difficult, but essential, to

17

keep a nonjudgmental third ear; otherwise the implicit social evaluations of the observer become the determiners of what is pathological and what is not.

Although we have generally become too sophisticated to place hasty value judgments on what is "good" or "bad" in behavior, it is easy to make another, less obvious error—to substitute, for psychological evaluations, judgments based on outside, or sociologically oriented, criteria. In the case of scientists, for example, it would be easy enough to assume that, merely because they are not a mental patient population and have seldom sought professional psychological help for personal or work difficulties—in fact, function excellently in their work—they are a nonneurotic or normal population. But we would then be using social criteria to determine what constitutes a psychological problem. The actual psychological status of these men must be subjected to the same diagnostic tools and evaluated by the same psychological and psychiatric criteria we would apply to other clinical material.

This, then, is the story of the development of a common denominator. It is the story of how the diversities and differences that characterize forty men—men of different ages, of varying family backgrounds, of different national origins—were channelized and directed so that the forty came to choose, as their professional work, scientific research. It is not a neat and congruent picture, but a piecemeal one. However, it is meant to be a study of the scientists rather than an artifact of the method of the study, and its piecemeal quality may have made the attempt more successful. Certainly, the book demonstrates that while some threads in personality development point to consistency and are tight-knit, others seem irrelevant, and perhaps thus express the constant fluctuations in the motivations of men.

NOTES

---

1. See, as examples, Margaret Mead and Rhoda Metraux, "Image of the Scientist among High School Students," *Science, 126*:384, 1957; D. C. Beardslee & D. D. O'Dowd, "The College-Student Image of the Scientist," *Science, 133*:997, 1961; H. Remmers, *The American Teen Ager.* Indianapolis: Bobbs-Merrill, 1957.

2. D. C. Beardslee and D. D. Dowd, *op. cit.;* and G. Holton, "Modern Science and the Intellectual Tradition," *Science, 131*:1187, 1960.

3. F. Redlich, "The Psychiatrist in Caricature: An Analysis of Unconscious Attitudes Toward Psychiatry," *American Journal of Orthopsychiatry, 20*:560, 1950.

4. The question of whether creativity will be destroyed during the course of psychotherapy—when everything one does or thinks is open to examination—is frequently raised by talented individuals who seek psychiatric help. There is little experimental evidence available on this, although I found, in a previous study on persons in the arts, that the characteristics of thinking and personality that distinguish artists are not the ones that get hardened into the neurotic patterns which have been so frequently identified with them ("Artist and Non-Artist: A Comparative Psychological Study," *Journal of Personality, 26*:13, 1958). Bellak appraises this problem from a clinical viewpoint in an interesting theoretical paper ("Creativity: Some Random Notes to a Systematic Consideration," *Journal of Projective Techniques, 22*:363, 1958).

5. Anne Roe, studying 64 scientists who were chosen as outstanding by their colleagues in their respective scientific fields, used similar clinical tools but different techniques of analysis and a different orientation to the problem (A. Roe, *The Making of a Scientist.* New York: Dodd, Mead, 1953). Since some of the factors in background and personal history that characterized her group also prevail in my sample, it is likely that my sample is representative of outstanding scientists, although I did not select them with such a criterion in mind.

6. In their book *Occupational Choice: An Approach to General Theory,* E. Ginzburg and associates point out that until the last ten years, two theoretical notions about work choice held sway: (1) an "accident" theory, which held that individuals make decisions about the future "accidentally," and that therefore the decisive factors cannot be evaluated; (2) an "impulse" theory, in which the individual's

selection of his field of work was thought to be determined by powerful, often unconscious impulses. Only recently has the development of general theories about vocational choice permitted the formation and testing of systematic hypotheses about the personality characteristics and motivations underlying selection.

7. Natural scientists may be interested in L. K. Frank's monograph, *Projective Methods* (Springfield, Ill.: Charles C Thomas, 1948), for in it he suggests that the recent developments in the physical sciences in the past fifty years—with the new assumptions and organizing concepts, the new methodologies and new criteria for credibility— are not only significant for the life sciences, and especially for psychology which has attempted to follow the methods of classical physics, but also offer a rationale and sanction for the procedures employed in the projective techniques that I used in this study.

8. E. Shneidman, in studying the application of the method of successive co-variation in interviews, has pointed out how the content of interviews changes as they are extended from one to a number of sessions.

9. Frederick J. Hacker first elaborated this notion in the *Proceedings* of the Conference on Perception and Personality, held at the Hacker Foundation for Psychiatric Research and Education in April 1957.

II

The Beginnings of Scientists

THE LIVES OF THIS GROUP OF SCIEN-tists span two generations and two continents. Among them, they speak twelve languages. Certainly, such differences in time and cultures contribute to diversity in personal remembrances. Some men knew a great deal about their parents and early childhood and were sensitive to the small dramas of everyday life. Others could remember only vague incidents and seemed to identify only slightly with important persons in their past. The historical material that follows testifies to the effects of milieu differences, the additional contaminating influences of personal propensity, and the incidence of distortion, repression, and omission that enters

21

into the process of recall of even men of science—although we like to think them free from such human idiosyncracy.

Some of the background data about the scientists and their families are presented in accompanying tables. In general, they are an American-born, urban-reared, forty-year-old, middle-class socioeconomic group. But these generalizations, and the data that deviate from them, do not seem the most meaningful way of looking at early histories; I decided, therefore, that rather than adhere to the formal breakdowns the tables suggest, I would look at how the scientists' attitudes toward work and achievement were influenced by their parents' personalities, occupational status, and socioeconomic background.

One striking finding stands out immediately: Nineteen of the 40 scientists (47.5 per cent) did not know their fathers very well. Four fathers had died early in their children's lives or had left home because of divorce when their sons were very young. Fourteen others either worked away from home or were so absorbed in their work that they were for all practical purposes absent most of the time. Ten of these were immigrants who had come to this country from Europe and had started small businesses of their own in the 1920's and 1930's. In other words, almost half the scientists had very little personal contact with their fathers. This sizable figure takes on added significance when compared with my findings from a previous study of 40 persons in the fields of painting, writing, music, and the theater arts. This earlier study revealed similarly that half of these artists had lost their fathers early in childhood (in contrast to a control group of men who had gone into business fields).

Neither the scientists who knew their fathers intimately nor the ones who knew them slightly liked them very much. Generally, the fathers were described as rigid, stern, aloof, and emotionally reserved. Some men interpreted their fa-

TABLE 1

GEOGRAPHIC DISTRIBUTION AND SOCIOECONOMIC LEVEL OF FAMILY

BIRTHPLACE	URBAN Socioeconomic Level[b]			RURAL[a] Socioeconomic Level[b]			TOTALS
	Low	Middle	High	Low	Middle	High	
Europe and Canada							
Men under 40[c]	0	1	0	0	0	0	1
Men over 40	0	2	1	0	2	0	5
United States							
Men under 40	6	10	3	1	1	0	21
Men over 40	4	3	2	1	3	0	13
TOTALS	10	16	6	2	6	0	40

a Rural, or cities under population of 10,000.
b Estimated from interview information.
c Age at time of data collection (September, 1957–March, 1958).

thers' aloofness as passivity or withdrawal; the hard discipli-
narians were described as embittered men who were reacting
to personal defeats. Five of the group felt their parents had
married very unhappily; three blamed their fathers' alcohol-
ism or gambling on their mothers' behavior. Only one sci-

TABLE 2

OCCUPATION OF PARENTS

Occupation	Fathers[a]	Mothers
Professional (other than science)	3	3
Science	3	
Business: small	19	5
large or corporate	5	
Semiskilled	3	3
Unskilled	4	1
Farming	3	
Housewife only	—	23
Assisted in family enterprise	—	5

a All parents were classified, including the 4 fathers and 2 mothers who died
when subjects were below ten years of age.

entist openly hated his father, who had beaten him physically until he was seventeen years old and had often embarrassed him in front of his friends. Another hinted that his father was very critical of his table manners, but quickly rationalized it by stating he was quite sure that his father's treatment of him was "pretty normal."

Some of the nineteen who have grown up without their fathers reflected the loneliness, disappointment, and rage that some mothers had voiced openly and others conveyed unconsciously. But the feelings about their fathers were not completely one-sided. Some took pride in their fathers' self-made success; others spoke of their rationality, of their logic and control in most situations. Among the group were the "typical Yankees," "typical New Englanders," or "typical Middle West farmers," represented as having the joyless rigidity commonly associated with these labels. Only occasionally did one consider his father very happy or contented. One European-born scientist said with great tenderness, "My father valued things other than money."

Whether paternal relationships are distant or close, happy or ambivalent, many aspects crop up in the later attitudes and behavior of children and get solidified in their adult identifications. Each scientist incorporated these relationships in his own psychological structure in a highly individualized way. Fathers in professional scientific work themselves, for example, left widely differing impressions of the profession with their sons. One father, a chemistry professor in a large university in this country, was at home only in his laboratory. His son said of him:

He was sort of an American-type man—all mild and beaten down by his wife. The only thing he was independent about was his work. He was very mild, good tempered, very logical and clear, and an extremely good teacher. My relationships with him in the laboratory and in going to school—I had him as a teacher in two classes, as a matter of fact, when I

24

was an undergraduate—were completely different from relationships at home. That's probably one of the reasons I became a scientist. Now, looking at it in retrospect, I think that when I saw my father in the laboratory, I thought, "This is a good way to be independent, to be a scientist."

This scientist felt that his father had never exercised any overt pressure to influence his son's career choice. He did recall, however, that when a brother wanted to go into a career in music, his parents had used disapproval and disparagement to discourage the choice. The brother ultimately became a chemist.

Another chemist, whose father had a Ph.D. in physics and worked as an electrical engineer, has adopted the identical intellectual work habits of his father:

My father is very much like me, actually. We have the same interests—well, for example, he's an extrovert—or at least, he's not a total introvert, but rather has very broad interests. He reads a good deal in history and philosophy, and he doesn't enjoy large groups of people any more than I do. He objects strenuously to having to go to parties during the week and, in fact, on week ends too, for even then he is an extremely hard-working man. Now, although he's retired, he still goes to Washington three days a week and consults. When he's home, he's almost too busy to do anything else. He's always up in his study working. I remember him when I was growing up. He invariably worked until ten, eleven, twelve; sometimes he might be reading, but a lot of times he'd bring work home from the office, and I do the same today.

Another scientist-father told his son scarcely anything about his work. The son says:

I don't know whether my father kept his work from me deliberately or not, but it must have been deliberate because

25

I know nothing about it. There were no attempts to interest me in any scientific thing. The only interest he ever showed was a deliberate attempt, when I was starting college, to guide my choice of courses—away from biology and into chemistry. I don't know if it had the effect he wanted, because in a way I think he was trying to scare me away from chemistry. But it did have the effect in one regard, and that is, that even though I went into biology, I came away with a great appreciation of chemistry and the need for it. I knew what my father did, but I had the impression that his work was not very stimulating. I think now it's an interesting part of science, and I would have thought so even then. It wasn't that he kept any secrets from us; it was just that he didn't fit in very well—he was an embittered person. He had started his career in chemistry, and this had been broken up by war. He left, became very discouraged, and always thereafter remained withdrawn and depressed. He'd sit without talking for long periods of time and would keep himself apart.

Ten scientists were sons of immigrant parents who worked hard and long to make a living. In a number of cases, work occupied both mother and father, especially where the fathers ran small shops. The children were left to their own devices and often felt that they scarcely knew their parents: "So much energy went into making a living," said one scientist, "that I think there was little time left over for any of us."

One chemist described going into the small grocery store his parents owned in New York City, sitting all day long on the barrels at the back of the shop reading books. He did not forget how miserably his parents eked out a livelihood:

I could not bear seeing my parents kowtowing to customers seven days a week and being so helplessly caught up in the store. My lack of drive in my own work is, I'm sure, partly related to that. It may be more immediately related, however—well, I noticed the change more directly when I came home from the army. The experiences there just made me feel that I wanted to work only at an eight-to-five job and devote myself completely to my family and to my other interests.

Some scientists called their immigrant fathers unfortunate, unsuccessful businessmen; one described his as an out-and-out failure.

One American-born father ran a hardware and grocery store in a small town in Wyoming. It was started during the depression; in order to make a go of it, the father had to give long-term credit to his customers, who were primarily low-income people and included a large Indian group from the neighboring Crow Reservation. The son said:

> Since it was illegal to sell liquor to Indians in all the Indian states, their primary purchase was, I remember, vanilla extract. And I always say that it was this vanilla extract that actually put me through college. For me, my father is a very distant—I started to say, a two-dimensional—person in my background. He's a pasteboard figure who was there and around, but with whom I had very little to do. I felt no sense of rapport with him and I never felt like confiding in him or establishing any emotional relationship. I never realized I had an emotional attachment to him until I became an adult.

The three fathers who were big businessmen provide another frame of reference toward work. Their sons—although encouraged to go into business—rejected it as a career for themselves because they wanted to make an independent choice. As one put it:

> I was always fairly independent and somewhat left-of-center in attitude. I remember very well the battle royal that used to occur at home when I would point out that my responsi-

bilities were not simply to provide children with food and clothing, but to make them citizens of the world, and I wasn't going to settle down in some mundane job and do this. It always ended up with their saying, "Oh, what a spoiled brat!" That's probably what I was. As far as I'm consciously aware, there wasn't a great deal of direction given me one way or another. No one seemed really to care. I used to think that people would have been happier with me if I had simply gone into my dad's business and followed along. The only time this was ever suggested was the summer before I was a senior—the time I was married. Dad did say, "Now, if you don't decide to go to school, you can come over to the brickyard." There was no encouragement, but I always felt the rest of the family would have been happier with me had I gone."

Occasionally a grandfather substituted for a father and was the more significant influence. One man describes his as an immigrant from Russia, who had come here at the age of twenty, leaving two children, and after a few years had gone back for his wife and family.

My father is an enormously energetic man, but my grandfather was more energetic and a businessman, and also had great intellectual interests. He had been brought up as a rabbinical scholar, had left Russia to escape when things became difficult for Jews, and then became interested in all kinds of things. All his life he was a terrifically strong personality and a terrible tyrant at home. He was the old-fashioned father of our family, and I think I more or less model myself on him. I think my haircut is his haircut. He looked like Theodore Roosevelt, and he was a man of very great energy and talent. I think by the time he was thirty or thirty-five he had become a millionaire. He just had that push. I think this is part of the background—this energy which one couldn't help admiring, and the enormous breadth of interest that most people who did the same things did not have.

The father's work was not the whole story for every son; there were some who scarcely knew what their fathers did. As one man said:

> I don't remember the very early days with my father. For one thing, my impression of him was that he was not a very friendly man, and I was pretty scared of him when I was a child. He was very big, very tall; in fact, he still gives me the impression that he could thrash me to a pulp if he ever wanted to. He was the kind of man who was interested in everything that happened, read a great many books, but wasn't particularly interested in the hustle-bustle of the world, which tended to isolate him from the outside world and from all of us children as well. I would say that 1931, when I was about fourteen, was the most critical year for me . . . my father went back to the farm to earn money to settle his debts. . . . For the next few years, my father was home only on week ends.

Some men, by contrast, had elaborate fantasies of fathers they never knew, built out of family lore and bits of their own memories. One chemist portrayed his father as a would-be doctor who, had he not married very early, might have been extremely prominent—at least, this is how his mother spoke of him. Throughout the interview, this man stressed that he had always felt he had to substitute for his very intelligent and potentially productive father. His mother's attitude made him feel very competitive toward this dead father, and he wonders today how much this has contributed to his ambivalence toward his work and to his doubts about the goals he sets for himself.

Another chemist felt his own strong drive for education could be traced to the father whom he scarcely knew. His father died when he was four, leaving his mother with five children, three older than himself, and one younger. He felt the necessity at an early age to become completely self-

29

disciplined in order to meet the demands of his impoverished and sparse environment. This self-discipline, he feels, has proved to be an invaluable asset for his work. He says, revealingly:

The Scotch and the Jews, from among the various religious groups that make up our country, put more emphasis on the importance of education than any other groups. My father was always taught that education was very important. His father had been a minister and a schoolteacher, and my father became a lawyer. He had this drive to use his hands, too, just as I do. He was quite a successful lawyer but quit law and went into farming. He wasn't quite so fortunate in the profession he picked in regard to providing his necessities. Well, my father educated my mother. My mother was a first-generation German, and the fact that my father educated her gave her quite a different education than you get from an institution. It followed the lines my father thought were important. I got some of the very same education, and the stress on education itself, for this was something my mother felt she had to pass on to us after my father died.

Still another chemist, whose father died when he was nine years old and whom he scarcely remembers, recalled that "my father wrote a letter to the editor of the Portland *Oregonian* saying that he had a son eight years old, or perhaps nine, that seemed to be very bright, and asked what he should do about getting books for him to read."

The association of "introversion" with "hard-working" cropped up frequently in the sketches of the fathers. However, one father, a self-made minister, was described as being a very extroverted, effusive man who played a prominent role in community activities. "I think he was more interested in people as people than in their souls or in any strictly or abstractly religious aspect of them. He must have had thousands of friends. This is my impression of my father." His son describes himself, on the other hand, as a completely different kind of person: shy, hostile, making only tenuous attachments to people. The son was a recluse as a child, ill at ease, and had "one hell of a time." He was like his cold and unsociable mother, while his brother was like the father. He envied both for "this golden characteristic, this affability and sociability, the ease and attachment to people."

The fathers seemed to exert little conscious effort in directing their sons' vocations. More immediate pressures were attributed to sociological exigencies. A number of the scientists came face to face with the depression; study at the university was the only possibility open to them when they graduated from high school. Many were also from cultural groupings that placed a high premium on professional work; it was taken for granted that sons would go to college, though the means for this were hard to come by.

Only one father in the group deeply wanted his son to be a scientist and devoted himself exclusively to the task of making him one:

My mother tells me that before I was born, my father told her that if she had a son, he would be a scientist; and he did it, not by telling me I had to be a scientist, but by showing me all kinds of things: how the ants work, what the moon was like, and all kinds of stuff—not telling me I ought to be a scientist, but how interesting everything was. Now that I'm older and can look back at the way he understood things, I realize he really understood science the way very few people do. He was not a scientist, but he had a real feel for what it was. For instance, he knew all the insects and what they did, but he didn't know the names of any of them; he didn't know the names of the stars or of this or that constellation, but he did know that the stars were great big balls of gas— he really understood. He would explain them and say, "What difference does it make what the name of the star is? In Germany, they'd call it by one name; the Martians would

31

call it by another name." So he'd concentrate on the theme, not on the way you'd describe it. In other words, he had a completely scientific mind.

My mother told me about a game he used to play after I had dinner. He had bought a lot of bathroom tiles of different colors. He set them up vertically on a highchair and when he got them all in a line, I had the fun of pushing them down. This is the way it would start, but there was a method in this game. He played this game with me every night, and after a while the game changed and became a little more complicated. It had to be a white tile and a blue tile, a white tile and a blue tile, so we had to be more careful; then it would be two whites and a blue, two whites and a blue, and if I wanted to put down two blues, there'd be a little excitement. And my mother would say, "Look at that poor child putting down two blues—no, no!" What was the idea of the game? Well, the idea was to get me interested in patterns and relationships, and that was the best he could do for a child who couldn't even talk, you see. That got me quite a mathematical mind because pretty soon I got quite good at that—two blues and a white, three blues and a white—you know, complicated arrangements. Then there were all kinds of things with numbers. By that time, I began to notice things: I noticed you could make sixes in several different ways and would report delightedly that there were so many different ways in which you could make a six. That's the way I got started in mathematics. . . . What's funny about this is that it is the most important feature I remember about my father. . . . I can remember my father as a nice man and all that—but all I can remember really is this rational line always. He was always that way about himself. For instance, when he would get sick or something, he would watch what was happening and what was going on, but to him it was like looking at a big machine. Like I remember when I was still a kid, and he got a cut—he only cut himself once that I recall. I don't know what happened—it must have been very serious because he was lying on the couch—but he was telling me about how all the white cells come, and what was going on in his body. He finally died from high blood pressure and a stroke. For a month or so before, he suddenly got a blind spot in his eye and said, "Hey! I've got a blind spot in my eye now. It's either in the retina or there's some dirt in the eye, or it's in the back of the brain. Let's see: if it's in the brain, it'll be the same for both eyes—it will be the same blind spot because it's the only way connections are made; but if it's in the eye, it'll be only one," so he closed one eye and fooled around and figured out it was in the brain. He said, "If it's in the brain, it's a blood vessel that's broken, and I'm pretty sure it may be a blood vessel somewhere else, and then I'll be dead." . . . For him, it was an exciting new experience to be able to figure out where it was and what caused it. He was so thoroughly and characteristically like that, that it's hard for me to remember any other aspect of his personality.

These interview data—and I have presented only a sample—show there are no common characteristics that describe all the fathers of these scholarly men, nor have these parents played one type of role in their sons' developments. Even what seem to be similar circumstances and psychological conditions for two given scientists, appear on closer inspection to have been incorporated by each in quite different and individual ways. Some of the sons appear to be replicas of their fathers in scientific guise; others seem to have rejected all similarity.

Analysis of the psychological test records corroborates the finding that the father's attitudes and personality features have usually found idiosyncratic expression in the son's psychological make-up.

The mothers of our scientists were occupied mainly with homes, children, and husbands. In Europe it was particularly difficult for women to assume any other role in the social structure of the early 1900's. This tightly defined framework, however, enclosed passive and silent women, some energetic and revolutionary ones, some who were protective and maternal. They all seemed to have great meaning for their children, although they were somewhat obscured in their more paternally oriented cultures. Only one of the European scientists spoke of his mother with ambivalence; the others described their mothers with affection and great admiration.

My mother was quite a different person from my father. She was quite artistic, would play the piano, and we always sat around and sang together. I was much closer to my mother than to my father. It was my mother who tried to keep the house happy. I always remember how she wanted me to learn to play the piano, and then I wanted to play because she wanted me to, but I was really too lazy, so I never learned the instrument very well. I was always interested in hearing my mother play. I associate almost everything I remember happily about my childhood with my mother.

Another said:

My mother was—well, I don't know whether you're familiar with Jewish life in small towns—women were not supposed to be educated, so my mother had no education whatsoever. She could read the prayers, and that's about all, but she was very clever and sensible. She was the one to whom neighbors always came for advice and suggestions when they couldn't get along. I remember many times a husband and wife would come to her, and I remember the lectures she would give them. She was always looked on with respect by others because of that. She was much more rigorous in decisions than my father; she made decisions quickly and more completely. My father was more tentative, never rushing things, but when she made a decision, it was carried through with the greatest precision and with the greatest of speed. It also had an influence on me. My mother died when I was sixteen, and I remember her very well.

American mothers represented a more varied background. As Table 3 shows, twelve of the mothers were unschooled, or educated primarily by their husbands; twenty-five had formal elementary or high school education; three were college graduates. A few of the children were raised by relatives or older sisters; a few were raised by maids and gov-

TABLE 3
EDUCATION OF PARENTS

Highest Education Level Achieved	No. of Fathers		No. of Mothers	
University:				
Ph.D. Degree	2		0	
Received B.A.	4		3	
B.A. Incomplete	1		0	
TOTAL UNIVERSITY:		7		3
High School:				
Graduate	12		8	
Incomplete	2		3	
TOTAL HIGH SCHOOL:		14		11
Grammar School:				
Graduate	2		3	
Incomplete	6		4	
TOTAL GRAMMAR SCHOOL:		8		7
Foreign Schooling (extent unknown)	7		6	
Parochial Schooling (extent unknown)	4		1	
None	0		12	

ernesses, especially when mothers had to carry sole financial responsibility, or worked side by side with husbands in their shops. One chemist said he never knew his mother because she left so early in the morning and returned so late at night.

35

Several used vague and offhand terms to describe their mothers, saying that they felt emotionally isolated from them even though they were not physically absent as much as the fathers were.

Two of the American mothers took in boarders to help supplement the family income—one was a widow, and the other was usually alone, for her husband worked on the road most of the time. In both of these cases, sons were aware of their poverty, and both men worked for a time before going to college. One mother demanded financial help from her son during high school and openly discouraged further schooling for him.

Only a handful of the American-bred scientists seemed to have made psychological peace with their mothers. A few expressed empathy with the fearfulness, the limitations, the language handicaps they saw in their mothers. More often the scientists depicted their mothers as being overprotective and possessive, immature, anxious and fearful, hysterical neurotic, and filled with psychosomatic complaints; or as being "too aggressive, too driving, and too uninvolved in us" and "too undemonstrative." A handful saw their mothers as wise, forthright, independent women.

A few realized their mothers' mark on themselves. One chemist said, for example, that his mother had always been frustrated in her love of music as a child. She had been brought up as a strict Mennonite and had always been rebellious against and resentful of the restrictions that this sect placed on its members. And yet he said:

> I guess she also placed this on me, and I'm a fairly rebellious kind of person in general. That's why this is a good profession for me—chemistry—because you have a lot of freedom. You can be very rebellious and get away with it, particularly if you're good. If you're good enough, you can get away with almost anything. There are very few good scientists, you see.

Another described his mother as a revolutionary sort of woman, a woman of great stamina and an enormous amount of energy. He said:

This is something I think I've inherited from her, and I'm thankful for all these genes that I have not selected. I'm sure if it were not for the holocaust in Europe, she would be still alive. In my home you didn't get the feeling of love so much because my mother was too occupied: she had to run the house and run the business. It was quite a bit in those days, but she did it with terrific efficiency, and I remember she was never sick. Though she was by and large illiterate, she had a certain sense of the need for education, and that was her ambition—that we should get not only a good but also a modern education.

One physiologist tells a significant story of his having essentially "two mothers": his own mother, whom he describes as a woman who had never matured beyond the emotional age of twelve, and a second mother, who was really a godmother but who played the major role in his intellectual life.

My own mother was a child in woman's clothing, a woman whose emotional gratifications were entirely dependent on her childish relationship to the world. To her, possession of things meant a great deal, but the satisfaction derived from them would last only for a short while. For my mother, I was a very good child, and by this I now know what was meant: I was somebody who didn't interfere with the situation. I'm sure my main desire at that time was to please her and make myself the ultimate possession that she could show off, so I could say in a way that I was almost pushed into doing something very well intellectually. "Pushed" is a hard word to use, I suppose, because I don't remember her demanding I ever do anything. The force was different, but it

37

was just as effective—the possessive, all-enveloping relationship.

Across the street from me lived a woman who was the wife of a physician. This woman was like my godmother. She had a house that was one of the most incredible museums of the late Victorian Period, a house filled with wonderful, magical things, like opium pipes, gourds, sharks' jaws, a large library—maybe five thousand volumes. This woman tried to read to me when I was still a very tiny infant. I was essentially her child, and she was my typical mother in the sense of her own desires. She lavished on me all the affection and desire she would have had for any child of her own, and now she represents, I suppose, the prime thread in my emotional life. This woman had the capacity to direct, to point out how one could begin, how one decided what was good and what was bad. She was my only opportunity to learn this.

The search for second or substitute mothers is repeated in a number of histories. One man, who describes his mother as an antagonistic and hostile woman who led a painful life and in turn inflicted suffering on everyone else, found a woman teacher of whom he became very fond, and who returned his affection. But many others, with difficult mothers, had disordered and unhappy childhoods. An example:

My mother was an extremely excitable individual. She had been married when she was about eighteen, with Dad twelve years older, which meant in effect that he raised her along with the children. By the time she was twenty-three, she had three children. Two of them—two boys—had been killed, and one died. This was a very severe shock, and while I sympathize with it now a great deal more than I did then, she never made any effort to overcome this blow. I was fifteen years old before seeing her in anything but a black dress. Although these events had happened twenty, thirty, forty years ago—something like that—they were constantly in the foreground. This was one of the many things that profoundly affected my attitude and the feeling of all of us children.

Although mothers were less identified with work than were fathers, they were not necessarily less identified with achievement. Despite the fact that half the mothers were described as being passive, insecure, frightened of the world, lonely, dependent, reserved, high-strung, and excitable, they were at the same time the ones who encouraged reading and intellectual pursuits. Often this was merely following cultural tradition, but they took their obligations about educating their children seriously.

The three mothers with college degrees actively identified with intellectuals who feel that energetic pursuit of the arts is the mark of a well-educated man. While immigrant parents sought to live out some of their own frustrated needs for schooling through their children, these educated mothers felt that they themselves were frequently the experts in training their young and they took to their duties with a dedicated, but often heavy, hand. One scientist described his mother's approach as "a disciplined one":

In my home, my mother was a very dominant person, and she was very much the boss. She decided what was good for all of us, and then insisted that we carry through with all these things, and insisted in a most emphatic way. She taught me at home for two years, so I didn't even start school until I was eight years old. When I started school, I started in the fourth grade. That's a very bad thing that nobody should ever do. My mother's teaching made going to school, at the beginning, altogether very dreadful. I remember going to school the first day when I was eight. I hadn't started taking piano lessons, and I didn't know anything about reading music. When I went to school, there they were sitting with this book open, and all these notes, singing and sight-reading. I hadn't the faintest idea what

39

this was about. I was floored, and it took me a long time to catch up in music. Then the next thing they did was arithmetic, and I didn't know what that was about, and I didn't know how to write very well. They all had learned to write according to Mr. Palmer's method, and I had learned only to print. The only thing I could do was read because my mother emphasized reading, and I could read much better than the rest.

So, I did badly in school and was always on the verge of being sent back to the grade below. My mother wouldn't stand for that. It was dreadful, so I hated school something terrible, and I didn't get any fun out of learning things. The only thing that was fun in school was when they started teaching us French.

My mother had been a high school teacher; as a matter of fact, she had her bachelor's degree in chemistry. My mother and father went to the same small university. She had taught high school on and off throughout college. She had very strong notions about how people should be taught. She figured she knew how to do this better than just those ordinary schoolteachers did. And so she started out with the notion that she should let her children have the benefit of this experience; but as she got to know the school system better, she was less repelled by it. I remember very clearly that I wanted to go to kindergarten so badly because a boy I knew went to kindergarten. My mother assured me I would not learn a thing, and that this was very bad, and that she could teach me better at home; but she changed her mind about that.

My mother also had the idea we were supposed to associate only with university people, intellectuals, and that all other people were uninteresting. I think both my parents had this attitude very strongly, but I remember my mother discouraging all of us very much from playing with other children who weren't the children of university people. She was tremendously afraid that we would get nonintellectual interests from associating with people outside the university world.

Another chemist remembers vividly how his mother would drive him to New York for plays, museums, and concerts. He says:

> I used to rebel greatly at going to these concerts. My mother never explicitly demanded that I go; it was just expected I would participate in what was offered to me in some implicit way. Both of my parents actually were interested in self-discipline, and the self-discipline with which I grew up was something that just came from the atmosphere of the home, I'm sure, more than anything else. This made me want to do well in school and get something out of it, and I never had to be rewarded for doing very well.

Like the fathers, then, the scientists' mothers apparently were not cast in any single mold. In general, the subjects regarded their mothers ambivalently. Some men hold intimate, warm, admiring pictures of them; others look at them coldly and rejectingly, their hostility coming out perhaps most openly in their search for lovable and loving substitute figures. As a group, the mothers stood for achievement and for personal development through education. For some mothers, this was in the spirit of complying with the traditions and values of their original cultural groups. For others, their sensitivity to missed or nonexistent opportunities and the resultant frustrations seemed to be the stimulus. We get only hints of how the strategies they employed to push their aspirations affected their sons' motivations, but these do suggest the highly individualized ways the maternal attitudes and behavior were internalized in the scientists' psychological structures.

There were few common denominators among the scientists during their growing-up years. The children raised in the older, stable culture of Europe described more homogeneous kinds of circumstances than did the Americans whose experiences depended on what part of the country they lived in, whether or not they were only children, how close their parents were to their original cultural groupings, and the nature of the family ties.[1]

Few scientists recalled their earliest years. In most cases their memories began with school days. Play, chores, and school have merged in a misty composite in their recollections, but their feelings about childhood suggest the nature of their experiences.

The European children spent about 95 per cent of their days in school, even from their first years, and only on Sundays, holidays, and vacations were they free to do much else. The only thing one man considered play was walking in the woods every day. When summer came, he regularly went to a spa in the mountains.

Another European scientist described his childhood, in the eastern Europe of the early 1900's, in this way:

We had not much time to play. Playing was, first of all, looked upon as a waste of time, and some types of play were looked upon as sin actually, and as a result we had very little play officially. In spite of that, and because we had many things around—like tools, trees, the river, and the forest—we had a lot of fun, I would say. I often compare this with the children now who have all of these toys that you wind up, and who run around so much. We were always busy. There were always projects, something to do. There were chestnut trees to grow or oak trees to harvest; there were lizards to catch or snakes to hunt—always something to do. There were dams to build on the rivers, the creeks, so that when we had time, we used it well. This was play of a different sort. It wasn't a game, but it involved association with other children because we played together. You see, we had no movies, no comic books, but there were things to do that were just as enjoyable to children as these things now— perhaps more so. For the thing that impresses me the most about children I see around is that they're very bored most of the time. I have children who come around to my garage now because I still like to work with tools and do a great deal of work. They come around; they're bored; in fact, I make my garage almost a play school, for I give them tools and let them work, and they enjoy it immensely.

Closely paralleling this European memory are the remembrances of a biologist who grew up during the 1900's in a semirural area in North Dakota.

I liked to hike and to hunt rabbits and to go on long walks, and I liked to do things mechanically. My father was a pretty progressive farmer when he was younger. He had a shop—a combination carpentry and blacksmith shop—and he was pretty tolerant of my activities in this shop, so I built a lot of things.

Also I read quite a bit as a youngster. I was not a reader like my son is now—he reads everything—quite advanced stuff, too. I never read to the extent that he does, but I read a tremendous amount of trash, like Horatio Alger books. They were the standard books—and I read these kid books by the hundreds.

Later, when I was old enough to be interested in scouting, I was very active in that. It was different from scouting today, which is highly organized, and kids are pushed into it and told what to do. In those days, we had to do it ourselves—generate our own interest. I probably provided some of the drive to keep us going and get the kids to come to meetings. Probably I was kind of an organizer, and I came to know lots of kids that way.

An urban childhood during the early part of the twentieth century (particularly for those with means), was more likely to arouse intellectual interests than a rural one. One man, for example, tells of growing up in his grandfather's home where there was an enormous variety of books on

43

"every possible" subject. He remembers long periods of looking at the pictures in the volumes before he was able to read, and he remembers the very happy times he spent there before he was grown up. He turned out to be an astrophysicist, and recalls fondly the works of a popular female author of the time who wrote on astronomy, and remembers how much his interest was aroused by the pictures in her books.

His adolescent life reflected the temper of the times—the "roaring twenties." He related how his father had gone for years to a beach resort on the New Jersey seacoast, and how he himself had entrée to all the leading speakeasies in that area. He gambled in the evenings and did all the things that:

> very young people would try to do, to imitate what we read about in the papers about Biarritz, Cannes, or Monaco. In those days, there was a lot of money in this particular area, and we were all very social and uninhibited people. We were the remnants, I suppose, of the "roaring twenties." I had a red wire-wheeled convertible, a Locomobile, when I was old enough to drive, and I used to tear around, and we all believed we were Hemingway characters—but that's a different part of my life. I suppose I had this rather different split life, so maybe I'm not a typical scientist after all.

No such incisive picture can be drawn for those in the group who were born at the time of World War I. They were chiefly from middle-sized or large urban areas, and their experiences seem characteristic of the mobility and fusion of these environments.

Twelve of the forty scientists grew up without brothers or sisters, or, if they had any, the age difference was so great that no close sibling relationship was possible. (See Table 4.) This seemed to produce a general tendency toward isolation. Some felt however that they tended to isolate themselves a

TABLE 4
FAMILY CONSTELLATION

Subject the	Number
only child	5[a]
oldest child	19
youngest child	9
other	7
Subjects who had one or more siblings working in science fields	4
in professional fields other than science	13
in arts	3
in business	7
in semiskilled	3

[a] In seven additional cases, the subject felt as if he were an only child because the age difference between himself and his siblings was so great.

result of their own needs for personal distance and removal from close contact. Those who had brothers of nearly the same age were intimate with them, though frequently this intimacy took the form of open competition or jealousy mixed with admiration, particularly when the relationship with parents was lukewarm and constricted.

Only a few of the scientists had much contact with their sisters. In European families, the sex roles were divided quite strictly. As one man describes it:

The division between girls and boys was very sharp. All the children had duties. I don't know exactly who did what any more, but the girls did certain tasks, and the boys did others. I guess that's something that has disappeared. In my youth, boys and girls were so separated that any kind of relationship with girls was almost out of the question. Boys played by themselves, and girls played by themselves.

The American scientists also reported hardly any contact or personal involvement with their sisters. One chemist

45

said that he had to become independent so as not to be pushed around by his four sisters. Yet the picture he cherishes most from his childhood is that of himself, his sisters and his parents in the living room, evening after evening each silently reading and munching apples. In the home where the father devoted himself to making his son a scientist, a daughter nine years younger saw no way of getting the father's attention other than by becoming interested in science herself, and she ultimately became a physicist.

Several of the subjects felt that they definitely had not been regarded as the bright child in the family. Five expressed envy and jealousy of brothers whom they idolized although ambivalently, for being more affable, congenial, or more athletic. A few hung on the coattails of the admired brothers, but many became "more ingrown," as one scientist expressed it.

More than anything else, the academic values and traditions of the family seemed to determine whether or not intelligence was highly valued. For example, the one child prodigy in the study was doted upon by his patriarchal grandfather because the boy could share his grandfather's wealth of interests, and this situation was paralleled closely by another man from an immigrant rural background. On the other hand, in those homes where brawn and hard physical work were highly regarded, or where money was at a premium, these bright children's intellectual aspirations were sometimes actively discouraged, and frequently they had to retreat from their families in order to protect their interests.

I found lonely, passive, withdrawn children; aggressive, rebellious, raucous youngsters; sickly ones; and those who described themselves as ordinary and who did seem unmarked by severe traumas. Their lives appeared to be similar in most respects to those of their friends and schoolmates

46

xcept for one feature consistently mentioned throughout the
nterviews: periods of isolation from the customary groups
vith which a child might be expected to identify—an isola-
ion sometimes lasting for years at a time. Occasionally this
vithdrawal was brought on by actual physical illness or dis-
bility, but more often these were merely periods during
vhich the individual felt emotionally distant from friends of
is age.

Seven were kept from mingling with other children and
etting about freely by physical isolation. Some suffered
rom severe childhood diseases; others developed visual or
uditory disturbances, which mechanical devices did not
ifficiently ameliorate; and some had handicaps which the
cientists themselves called psychosomatic. Here is how one
escribes his illness, for example:

I had a physical disability that was diagnosed as some sort
of heart trouble, and restricted my athletic endeavors until
my senior year in high school. I don't really understand
what happened there, but the disability suddenly disappeared. It started because I had been overdoing in some
way—swimming, I think, with some kids in a public pool.
I swam too much, had some sort of a collapse, went to bed,
and there I was for several days—maybe a week or so—but
during that time the symptom of the thing was that the
heartbeat would become terribly increased in rate, and
then wouldn't slow down. As I lay there in bed, I was under
the impression that I could willfully slow down the heartbeat just by concentrating on it. I had a long period of that;
but after reaching high school, I had no trouble with it and
used no restraint in physical activities. . . . Humorously,
when I took my physical for the Army—they asked me if I
had ever had any childhood diseases. I told them I was
supposed to have had rheumatic fever resulting in a heart
condition. The guy just laughed at me as though I were
trying to malinger, so I never mentioned it again.

47

This man's father, incidentally, developed a physical ailment at the same time which made it necessary for him to change to more sedentary work. Another subject who was a childhood asthmatic remarked that his mother was "full of psychosomatic ills."

One chemist, who came down with rheumatic fever at about fifteen, called his illness "a blessing in disguise." He said that since his heart was affected, he was "slapped into bed" for almost a year, and that this had the most profound effect upon his intellectual development. He started to read a great deal and to work on mathematical problems. When he got back to school, where he had previously done poorly, he became one of the best pupils.

The children with sensory loss disturbances were perhaps the most isolated of all. One described his illness in this way:

I was always tall, thin, and rather gangling. . . . As a child, I had trouble with my eyes, probably from too much reading—I don't know. When I was in sixth grade, the trouble became so severe that I became quite nervous for awhile and had to be sent to the desert to recuperate. At about this time, too, I had difficulty with my hearing. This happened when I was very young. I don't know whether it happened with scarlet fever or what, but one day I woke up to find my hearing poor, and my eyes bad. The whole thing left its mark on me because I had to be sent away; then when I came back, I had to begin lip-reading classes for hard-of-hearing children that are part of the curriculum in the schools for the handicapped; essentially, I was treated as a handicapped child. I wasn't given much chance to adjust to the situation. It took many years, but now I've adjusted pretty much to it. I still have no idea what caused it.

Another chemist, who had a congenital hearing diffi-culty, describes himself: "I busied myself because I couldn near well in a group of children, so I spent a lot of time worrying about what I now know are insoluble intellectual problems."

One man tells a fascinating story of how he overcame a severe childhood lisp. I quote it in detail because the seemingly spontaneous transformation of a disabling neurotic difficulty into a valuable character trait merits psychological study in itself.

I spent a great deal of my time as a child out of doors and by myself. I suffered from a speech impediment that involved a great deal of stuttering and a very pronounced lisp which I still have to a certain extent. Children poked fun at me, and this made me more retiring. Also, I never did excel in football or baseball. Physically, I was not exactly weak, but I was one of the children that bigger boys could beat up on. Then something happened during the war which I think could not at all have been predicted when I was a child. I suddenly found out I was a damned good public speaker. The first discovery was made in New York when I was forced into making a speech unexpectedly at a big luncheon at the Waldorf-Astoria Hotel. There were all sorts of important people at the luncheon—literary and political leaders, for example—people I'd heard about and read about only in magazines. All of a sudden, I had to get up and give a speech outlining some of the problems. I was petrified. I had no notes and no manuscript, but I gave a ten-minute speech. I still can't explain why, but it had a fantastic effect on the audience. I found when I was halfway through that I could feel this, and I found I could make them react or not react. I found that I had a power—a very interesting feeling. Then I was asked if I would go on a lecture tour to speak about the same problems, which were related to the use of the atomic bomb. I was young and idealistic, and agreed to do this. This was quite an experience for me, not only because I learned about people and

49

found I had this power to sway them but, most amazingly, because the stuttering dropped out spontaneously.

For a number of others, isolation resulted from obesity or skinniness, or physical weakness. Ten described themselves as being poorly co-ordinated and physically below par, with the result that they were often rejected by the quick and able children who chose teams and gathered the strong around them. Today, many look back on these disorders as childhood neurotic disturbances and classify them on the same level with nail-biting, psychosomatic illnesses, and speech disorders.

Some suffered from racial or religious discrimination and prejudice, especially in schools where they stood out as single members of minority groups. Three felt that their brightness had evoked physical cruelty from other children. One Jewish chemist said that he purposely put his good wits to use at age ten to form an astronomy club, which he then used as a successful wedge into the class from which he had been excluded.

This commonality of isolation may not seem significant in itself. What is important, however, is that such experiences invariably led the scientists to look to their own resources for solace and amusement. What they did by themselves varied according to age and individual interest. There were collectors, tinkerers, heavy readers, those who solved mathematical puzzles, and chess players. But what they did seemed not so crucial for later work as the fact that they had searched for resources within themselves and became comfortable being by themselves.

Often there was no goal set, no product, no result at the end; they played for play's sake. Some merely spent hours in daydreaming or toyed with ideas and symbols. What they gained was the enjoyment, the intrinsic satisfactions in the activities, and the fun of testing.

Not all of these scientists were model children. Three described themselves as rebellious and obnoxious, full of mischief and, more often than not, full of resentment. These three had been estranged from their mothers: one by death, one by chronic illness which prevented the boy from knowing her at all; one was the last son of a mother still grieving over deaths of her other children. Teachers, governesses, and gardeners took the brunt of their hostilities until adolescence, at which time fathers were openly resented, and the "adolescent revolt" became the socially accepted battleground.

One chemist says he spent a fair amount of his high school career in shooting pool, playing golf, or drinking beer. He said, as he stood in line to register for the university, a friend remarked, "You know, it was certainly a good thing the pool hall didn't open until nine o'clock, because if it had, neither one of us would actually have gotten out of high school." This man said that in one month in high school, he had been absent about twenty-seven days, yet had nothing but A's and B's on his report card. He is not sure to this day if the fact that his father was President of the Board of Education had anything to do with his remarkable record.

There were child poets in the group, child artists, budding journalists and photographers, enthusiastic and not-so-enthusiastic musicians, and sportsmen. Most of the American boys who were good at sports were sand-lot players. Basketball and tennis also attracted a large number. One European youngster found his way to friendship with his American schoolmates through his prowess at soccer.

Few of the scientists were more than transitorily preoccupied with collecting, which one of the physiologists in the study defined as "the sort of acquisitiveness that goes under the guise of science to the child." Even chemistry sets were much less significant than would be expected. One of the collectors described his interest in this way:

51

My great uncle, who was running the family business, was to me a very nice, rich, old gentleman. He had a bent for natural history. [Probably as a result of this influence] I used to collect odd things: birds' eggs, shells, fossils, fish, and put these into what I called "my museum." His daughter had the most fantastic collecting instinct of anyone I knew. There's a strong collecting instinct in my paternal family, which for me has been the dominating one—at least, it was in my early life. Also, my grandfather, who was a pear rancher, was an amateur scientist, a naturalist, very fond of the Sierra Nevada Mountains. I used to go with him a lot, and in those days that was quite an adventure. I can recall that he had a nice place with books on natural history which I still have now. He kept records of all his crops, of his own canning, and was an amateur photographer, too. I can't remember when I wasn't encouraged by my family into collecting and studying natural phenomena; but today I hardly do any of that at all.

The only tie-up between childhood collecting and a true attempt at scientific work was a paper, written by one subject at age ten, which was based on a collection of pictures of fish which a Dutch manufacturer had put in a box of cookies. The paper was about the habits of two rare inland fish.

Reading engaged all subjects more or less at some period, but even here there was variability from one to another in how absorbing an interest this became, and in what they read. One scientist's childhood home was practically a library; the family of another, however, openly discouraged reading, lest he ruin his eyes. One boy got a present of books for every birthday, but another had to sneak books into his house because his father would make fun of his having spent money on them:

Certainly my parents found it difficult to understand why I would save up pennies and spend $5, which was a lot of money in those days and under those circumstances, for a book I happened to be interested in. That was just beyond their comprehension. I might say that my father couldn't understand it any more than my mother, but I think my mother was more permissive in this respect. My father would have been angry if he had caught me spending money on books. There was no hesitation to interrupt me if I happened to be reading; in fact, I felt I had to hide away, for if I were out of sight, then things wouldn't crop up for me to do.

Reading did turn some toward science, but others were interested in foreign literature, plays, and the classics, or were drawn toward Greenwich Village where they hoped to become writers, dramatists, or members of stock companies. Literary Bohemia had all the enchantment that science did not unfold until later years.

One further note: seldom did these men engage in organized play. Only a few of the scientists were members of Boy Scouts, Woodcraft Rangers, or the community clubs so typical of the settings around which most boyhood activities are centered today. Occasionally, some enthusiasm for boyhood activities was fostered through small clubs at school, but even these school clubs were usually described as being rather transient; they lacked formal planning, and they were not a part of the curriculum required by school authorities.

Intellectually, most of the men showed high abilities at an early age. This innate ability was reflected in their school record; they skipped grades, got top marks with little effort, and two entered college at the age of fifteen. If no premium had been placed at home on excellent abilities, the rewards and commendations of the school usually compensated for this, and a number of men mentioned becoming attracted to teachers who both saw their promise and returned their affection.

53

The Europeans worked hard and long hours as students, were very dedicated to their studies, and often thought that school was an ordeal. They felt that one had to be extremely able in order to do well. As one man stated, "In Europe, it was not so fashionable to be happy in school as it is here. You were there to learn something." Another mentioned that any student who showed promise was especially disciplined—not unpleasantly, because this was recognized as appropriate for his abilities.[2]

By contrast, the American students thought school easy and mentioned how little stimulation there was until college. Most of them rose to the top of their classes—if not in the earliest years, by the end of grade school. For some, however, the motivation for doing well was not provided by the classes themselves. Special, advanced high school classes (at the Horace Mann School in New York, for example) gave some of the students their first stimulating and competitive experiences. But others became interested in academic subject matters quite independently and outside the classroom. Drive for excellence became for some an intense internal demand: "I was very conscientious about school," said one scientist, "and got upset if anyone knew anything at school that I didn't know. It would seem wrong to me. I liked to study, and I read everything I could get my hands on."

Another said:

I was good in school, but unaware of it. I had the curious idea that it was unfair to study, that schoolwork was only to test your innate ability, so I constantly tested myself. I thought nothing should ever be prepared beforehand or practiced. I had to be perfect, so I studied hard from the beginning. When I came to school, studying hard was a tradition. I was always scared when I started any new course, and only after I did excellently and knew how I stacked up with the others did I become less anxious.

The fact that high school was absurdly easy for one chemist made him feel that school played no role in his childhood. He said, "The greatness of the world lay in my own efforts, which were external from school, since I already knew what school wanted me to learn." Although this man had little respect for his teachers, on the other hand, the inadequate teacher drew quite a different response from one biologist, who said:

My chemistry-physics teacher in high school just didn't know beans. She didn't know much about chemistry or physics, and I realize it now, but at that time I didn't. She was just a girl out of college who had to teach the stuff; but somehow, she stimulated you. She let you go in the laboratory, fiddle around, and do things, and she wouldn't say, "No, no, don't do that or it will explode!" Sometimes it did explode. Fortunately, it didn't kill any of us.

Later on in college, I had another teacher who was a terrible teacher and a terrible scientist. Yet this fellow—he's famous internationally—influenced more people than almost anyone you could put your finger on. He was a terrible teacher. He taught genetics; I knew more genetics than he did, but the interesting thing is that he realized it and used to say to me, "I can't solve these problems. See if you can do them." It might have been a technique, but the fact is that he really couldn't do them, and he was willing to be frank about this. Now there is nothing that can hop a kid up more than to say, "Gee whiz, I can do them, and the prof can't," although they were really very simple. He couldn't do them because he just wasn't smart in this particular way. I've talked to many people about how he influenced person after person, and it's hard to see why because everything about him was wrong.

We often think that the tender and interested teacher who is long on human qualities serves as the most positive kind of influence, and many scientists' recollections support this notion. But one man described as most influential an eighth-grade teacher who "bullied me badly—a man who had an enormously strong personality. He scared me about my own abilities. I had a rough time with him, but I admire strong personalities, and he had one." This is the physicist who marveled over the strong personality of his grandfather, whom he had taken as his own model.

A few in the group felt that they had been thorns in their teachers' sides, and some performed in a lazy and erratic way, managing to irritate both their teachers and their parents. Almost all recognized how proud their parents were of their easy successes and achievements, whether they had actively approved of higher education or not.

I suspect that, in retrospect, the subjects see their science teachers in sharper focus than their English or history professors, because of the great personal meaning that science has since taken on. These incidents highlight some early turnings to science:

When I was thirteen and was a sophomore in high school, I had had a course in general science that was not a bad course and involved a little chemistry. I was walking home one day from high school with a boy I had known very distantly in grammar school, and he said, "Would you like to stop by my house and see some chemical experiments?" He was thirteen years old at the time, and he showed me these experiments which interested me so much that when I got home that night I found a book on chemistry that had belonged to my father who had died when I was nine. He had beeen a druggist. I began reading this book, got an alcohol lamp that my mother had around, began boiling things and mixing things together. I had some glassware largely from a man who lived next door who was a curator in a dental college, and I bought some chemicals, scrounged, got them from various places; and from that time on, I was a chemist. I remember that I had started collecting things when I was eleven or twelve, and had taken out a big book on minerals from the library and had copied out the tables for determining the nature of minerals—the tests you use—the hardness tests, etc., but it was this experimental thing that sold me on science.

Another man said:

I think the dominating factor in getting me oriented toward science was a teacher, a woman teacher I had in junior high. She was a practical kind of woman who took an interest in my welfare at that time. She would, for example, let me help her set up experiments that we had in general science in junior high, and she would let me fool around in the stock room. By that time, I had become interested in chemical sets and reading, and I read practically everything I could get my hands on. I had another very interesting teacher. Most of the children didn't like him—they thought he was sort of crazy—but I did. Again, he was one of those men who would let me poke around in the stockroom and would talk to me from time to time. As a result, I seemed to feel he had taken a personal interest in me. By the time I took chemistry, I found it very easy because I had helped my brother get through chemistry a couple of years before that.

While some scientists felt themselves influenced a great deal by teachers, just as many disclaimed being stimulated by them at all. This may be merely a lack of effective teachers, but it may also be related to the fact that a particular individual was not receptive to such influence or to his need to appear now as a self-made man. One does not customarily think of "self-made" as an important image for the scientist, but some scientists expressed as much pride in this self-reflection as do business tycoons who have fashioned their image after Horatio Alger. Some teachers did foster independence, for work in the laboratories after classes was often like an after-school job, so that when a student took on one of these, he also assumed assignments and responsibilities. Who can say how deliberate such teaching was?

There were always teachers who took a little interest in me. The teacher of chemistry in the high school said to me that if I had time and would like to do it—well, first, while I was in his high school chemistry course, he asked me if I could stay after school for an hour one day and help him determine the calorific value of coal and oil used in the public schools. He needed an assistant in this job using the Bond Calorimeter, and I did that. Then he said that perhaps I could keep on working in the lab after I finished the year's course, and I did for another year continue to work in the lab, come in every day for an hour—perhaps not every day—and carry out some things he assigned to me in analytic chemistry, and organic. Then, when I left high school without graduating, and got my transcript so I could go to college, I found he had given me credit for the second full year of chemistry. That was unusual.

Also pertinent to the scientists' personality development were their emotional struggles for independence—struggles which did not necessarily go hand-in-hand with the intellectual.

One becomes an adult in Europe very much earlier than here. At the age of nine, I started to read the Jewish books, the Talmud, and even learned at that time about the menstrual period because one volume is devoted to that. You age earlier. By the age of thirteen, you're responsible. That has its virtues; it has its faults; it ages you too quickly, and I had to make up for it in later life. I had to get some boyhood fun later. But in many ways I was rather pleased to be considered an adult and to be able to do certain things.

Another European, however, of different cultural background, stayed close to home until "bourgeois notions about not living at home in order to show independence when you start at the university" forced him to move under another roof in his home town.

Each of the older group of Americans made a point of telling about his need to assert himself in order to go to college or into a field he had chosen.[3] This often seemed to mark the break with his immediate family. In only a few of the younger men, however, were the struggles for independence so well defined. About half left home permanently once they went to college; some expressed their independence earlier. "At an early age, in my very early teens," said one man, "I would say I expressed my independence, and my parents were very careful not to tell me what to do. They made a point of not telling me what to do, and whenever they did try to discourage me from something—telling me not to go to college because of finances, for example—I did what I wanted." On the basis of the psychological tests, however, a small percentage of the younger scientists seem to have still to pull up their emotional stakes.

The eight men who were forced to work during adolescence because their fathers were dead or away or ill felt that work had put them on their own. One said that at twelve he and his brother had no one to tell them what to do, were forced to find ways to earn money, and after work would stay out at night, school or not, until 1:30. One took pride in how closely he could divide his day between work and school; another said his back-breaking work in canneries made him determined to get a "white collar" education.

Only two scientists traced their political development to their adolescent years. One recalls that his mother guided his reading in a political direction. She would start reading a book to him, was "sweet enough" to get him interested, and then left him to finish the book himself. "She particularly liked Shaw," he said, "so I read most of Shaw. Of course, he's pretty political minded, and this led to a lot of other reading, so that by the time I went to college, I was politically as developed as I am now. I haven't been interested in politics since. Once you get the principles, you can do quite well in a casual way."

For another man, however, politics was not to be flirted with casually. Raised in Europe, he had gone to a parochial school where one of his teachers had interested him in youth movement activities, which he now views as the most profound influence in his social and intellectual development. He describes attending conventions in Poland:

The conventions were tremendous things. Hundreds of boys and girls got together and had serious discussions on all kinds of questions. We reached conclusions about such things as the ideological backgrounds for youth, and how to raise children, and the whole problem of children in society, and all sorts of questions about socialism. It was a socialist group essentially, and there was a struggle going on then within the movement, as to whether it should remain apolitical or have a political implication. It was closely allied with the idea of developing a homeland in Israel, and everyone felt a pressure to go there as soon as possible.

I remember very well what one of the teachings of this movement was: "Don't listen, my son, to the ways of your father, for the ways of your father are, 'slowly, slowly'; the teachings of your mother are, 'carefully, carefully'; but listen to the storm that comes from behind." I should not give you the impression that this was a movement that took place in the lives of the majority of youth; it certainly didn't. I don't know how many participated, but it grew into quite a venture. Some people remained with the organization until the time of the Nazi invasion. Since these were all people who believed in rebelling and fighting for rights as human beings, not giving in, they were the leaders of the Polish uprising and died with it, but they died a heroic death. That was quite a chapter they've written in history.

Most of the subjects found college an exhilarating experience. For an idea of what aspects of college experience became meaningful to some of the subjects, we have the following recollections.

One man, who had felt lost in high school, and who had gone to college only because a community organization provided scholarships for him and his brother, tells of his first days:

It was an ideal setting in New England. I remember particularly the tall maple trees, the old Colonial houses, the taverns, the coach-stopper—or whatever it was called—all from Colonial days, and the surrounding country with its dirt roads, farms, and woods. It was homespun—an unluxurious kind of setting for the college. The thing that attracted me most was walking in the country around there. In the fall, all the people went out for cross-country because they felt it would build up their running muscles even though they weren't good at cross-country. We used to run through this area and did a lot of walking and exploring of long-deserted houses. My brother and I were elected to a fraternity in the first two years we were there, but then our antisocial and intellectual interests and activities made a number of us decide to rent an apartment. There was one man who stood out in our group, a wonderful guy, devoted to music. . . . He drank more than the rest of us, played his music, and this created to a small degree *la vie bohème* —the goal that I had dreamed about so frequently in my early youth. However, I also worked steadily and without strain; and as I think about it, it was the first time I was enjoying myself. I took a lot of courses I didn't need. I remember how I even continued to take French, which I had gotten into earlier, and how one of our intellectual friends used to go over to Paris every summer, come back with a trunkful of paperbacks which we would then read all through the winter. I worked through that French

61

program for four years and was quite fast at reading French at the end of it, but I haven't kept it up."

Another's experience:

I liked M.I.T. because it was flexible enough that you could take advanced things to get ahead. I did a lot of that. I was always at the head of the class and learned most of the stuff myself. After I had learned it by myself, the classes and courses would fill in a little here, a little there, but most of the time the stuff I would work on in the classes was something I had learned already, so that I could do it easily. I spent most of my spare time with a friend who was at about the same advanced level as I; we would talk all the time, walk together constantly, and that was the greatest adventure of all. When we first met each other, we were a little uneven in background. He had learned more about one aspect of physics than I had, and I had learned more about one aspect than he, so I taught him all I knew, and he taught me what he knew. It took us a few weeks to get even. Then every time we learned anything or saw something exciting, we told each other. We taught each other this way, and this was very stimulating. Most of our spare time, we spent doing things that were outside the school curriculum, but had to do with science.

Another man emphasized how he devoted himself to intensive research work even as an undergraduate:

My financial situation when I first went to college influenced my later college career. What I mean is that when I went to college, my father said that I could go if I wanted to, he would help me pay for board and room, but that was all he could do. As a result, I started out with a full course, but had to work in a bakery every night in order to make my tuition and costs. During the first quarter, I did pretty well, but my school work gradually dropped off. In my second year, the only subject I did well in at all was chemistry. In all the other subjects I had C's and D's—generally, all of my grades in college were poor. When I was in my sophomore year and had taken this one chemistry course, the prof wanted somebody to do research work during the summer. At that time I was spending days at the beach, and working nights at the bakery, so even though he paid only $25 for the whole summer, I took the job. This was the beginning of rather intensive research work on my part as an undergraduate. I had in all, I would say, five years of undergraduate research work. It's hard to imagine the environment at my university at that time; it was an unusual one compared to what the university is today because it has grown so much. Although it was a large and first-rate university, it had no graduate students, so the place was like a vacuum from the viewpoint of having people to do research. They were avid then to take on anybody who would do research and practically pulled students in from the halls in order to get it done. As a result, by the time I got my Bachelor's degree, I had the equivalent in experience and know-how of a Ph.D., but, of course, I hadn't had the course work. I even had four papers published as an undergraduate. But I was not a good student, and I was turned down by many graduate schools when I applied to them. Another thing that was very good about the setting at the university was the caliber of teachers. They were something special, the type you certainly don't have any more on an undergraduate level. And you had the kind of intimate contact with them that is now almost exclusively limited to graduate students with whom they work.

A few married during college. As adolescents, the men had meager contacts with girls; they were generally shy, bashful, and inhibited in their relationships. Eight married the first girls they were interested in, and a number of others could easily recall the girls with whom they had gone before they were married. Although I did not ask specifically about sexual experiences, a few alluded to their heterosexual behavior in adolescence and college years. Again, their experiences seemed to be minimal. One man attributed an unhappy first marriage to his youth and naivete: "I misinterpreted the sexual urge for love."

Beginning with their undergraduate days, the group's scientific experiences became increasingly similar. Graduate training provided the mold of professional research work to be followed.

From this point on, these men are no longer scientific novitiates but men who have taken on the frames of reference, values, and goals of the adult researcher, and who have incorporated these as part of their own mature identities.

To sum up the developmental data: Our search has been for single factors from the historical material that would stand out as absolute prerequisites for vocational choice in the sciences. None emerged, nor did any configuration of variables seem critical for this decision. Perhaps this finding was made inevitable by the orientation toward the single variable—an approach which is in line with classical scientific thinking. I suggest this because only recently Warren Weaver has pointed out that it may not be possible to isolate single factors for systematic variation in dealing with biological phenomena; perhaps one must begin to think in terms of what has been called organized complexities. This seems to have pertinence for psychology, where the significance of an event is known to rest on its relationship to the environment of which it is a part, and to the genetic-historic background of its occurrence.

Even in the case of traumatic events, fixations, and seemingly isolated and unique incidents, one can only point to specific phenomena as triggering mechanisms to which subsequent behavior can be traced. Yet such questions as why the incident serves as the trigger in the first place, and how to explain the nature of the reaction that took place, cannot be answered out of the personal and larger socio-historic context.

What the developmental material tells, then, is that there was greater diversity of experience among the men than similarities, that their backgrounds ran the gamut of geographical distribution, of socioeconomic backgrounds, of parental occupations, and of racial and religious grouping.[4] Attitudes of and relationships with parents, relatives, and teachers contributed to this variability and resulted from it. More important, the effects of their influence found highly individualized expression in the personality development of the scientists; I have found that developmental situations that appeared similar on the outside resulted in manifestly different influences upon the lives of individual men.

A number of significant findings emerged from the biographical data: First, the group is one in which excellent intellectual abilities existed, which were often recognized early, and subsequently led to gratifying experiences and relationships. For most men, excellent natural endowment was given encouragement by experiences that tended to place a premium on intellectual abilities, and which thus helped crystallize these overvalued activities in vocational choice and performance.

Second, most scientists experienced periods of isolation, either stimulated by personal needs or forced by physical or psychological circumstances, during which they turned or returned to their own resources for solace and amusement, experimented with their abilities, and extended them. Often the experimentation became rewarding and strengthened their interest in using these abilities. However, this reduced interest in "normal" children's games and activities.

Third, almost one half of the group was fatherless— their fathers dying early, or working away from home, or remaining so aloof and nonsupportive that their sons scarcely

65

knew them. Mothers were identified more with achievement, but relationships with family members were generally of a fragile and tenuous quality, and not too many scientists look back upon their parents and siblings with warm and positive feelings.

Fourth, these men turned away from their families, usually during adolescence or when they started college; some even cut off all but the most superficial ties, and then they went off on their own.

Fifth, the social histories of these men explode the myths of the all-important teacher or the absolutely essential chemistry set as being crucial factors in stimulating early interest in science. The myths operated in some cases, but in more instances these presumably criterial stimuli were absent.

NOTES

---

1. Strodtbeck's study of Jewish and Italian subcultures in the United States, for the clues in their value systems and family life which are related to their production of achievant individuals, pointed to these three values as important for the American achievement ethic: (1) a belief that the world is orderly and amenable to rational mastery; that, therefore, a person can and should make plans which will control his destiny; (2) loyalty to a larger collective than the family, which implies a willingness to leave home to make one's way in life; (3) a preference for individual rather than collective credit for work done. A good deal of the interview data these scientists have provided suggest that such ideals underlay their socio-history patterns. Strodtbeck also found that a power balance in the family is of importance in giving a child ideas which bear on his later success and failure—with the children believing what their parents do, and not what they say. (Family Interactions, Values, and Achievement, in D. McClelland, *et al, Talent and Society,* 1958.)

2. Malcolm S. MacLean pointed out to me how the differences in reactions between the American- and European-schooled scientists telescope the larger cultural differences that exist in their attitudes toward education.

3. G. B. Shaw has said that "breaking loose" means for some to leave family and friends, business and home, and avoid the danger of success without identity, of a success unequal to their unconscious ambitions.

4. Anne Roe's sixty-four eminent men in the biological, physical, and social sciences were generally of middle-class families and represented a varied economic background which spread over a wide geographical distribution. In these respects, my group parallels hers. Both of our samples, however, diverge from the subjects who participated in the *Fortune* survey (October, 1948) which drew a fairly mobile lower income level group—that did, however, range into the professional classes. While R. H. Knapp and H. B. Goodrich's data (*Origin of American Scientists*, 1952), derived from the information in the *American Men of Science*, from 1881–90 and 1931–40, did not permit precise socioeconomic categorization, they implied that a lower middle-class, nonurban, Mid-West background which had respect for intellectual values was most favorable to scientists.

Roe found a very high percentage (53%) to be sons of professional men, none of unskilled laborers, and only two of skilled workmen. Her group came from homes where intellectual interests were developed early. There was also a high proportion of first-born children, or children with a wide span in age between them and the next siblings. In all these respects, except professions of fathers, my subjects were substantially like hers. S. S. Visher, whose data were compiled from *American Men of Science*, 1906–1944, similarly found a high percentage of professional fathers among leading scientists; less than 1% of the fathers were unskilled workers. In his sample, two-fifths were the oldest in their families, but well over the majority of families had more than one child.

Though such external criteria were not the bases for selection of my group, they line up well in these respects with Roe's men. This suggests that in background, at least, they are representative of scientists chosen with an eye to distinction in their fields.

Some of my developmental information also generally conforms with her findings. Both groups tended to be isolated from their peers during some phase of childhood, for example. Also, one-fourth of her biologists lost a parent early. The bulk of evidence in this direction makes this a worthy bit of material to be added to the clinical studies already in progress in Chicago and San Francisco on persons who had lost a parent in early life.

67

III

The Scientists' Personalities

Certain common notions about the personality of the scientist crop up repeatedly in psychological literature; they are shared by psychologists representing various theoretical backgrounds. These concepts have to do with the way scientists meet their emotional challenges, with the behavior patterns that are found regularly in their personality make-up, with their conflicts, with the motivations to which they respond. The interpretations are couched in hypotheses which may take the form of descriptive terms thought to be correlated with the fact of being a scientist, or they may be elaborate psychodynamic formulations which look for a *primum mobile* to account for the scientist's functioning.

In order to test the most commonly held hypotheses concerning the psychology of the scientist, I selected the variables referring to emotional behavior, personality structure, and motivations which appeared repeatedly in the literature on these creative persons. Then, using the personality data on each scientist that the projective test instruments provided, the judges did a blind rating on these characteristics in the subjects. The results showed that there were a number of personality features which all the subjects shared. In this chapter I shall discuss these, turning to the interview data for information about how these commonly held personality features seem to be reflected in behavior, and especially how they contribute to scientific performance.

However, before presenting these results on the group I should like to give examples of the kind of personality pictures from which these common features emerged. In a comparative study such as this, one can lose sight of the fact that we have been studying forty individual persons, each of whom has developed unique ways of behaving, reacting, remembering, interpreting situations. Instead, in looking at the group as a whole, we tend to focus on variables that can be isolated and that still retain their meaning; and on variables that tend to characterize the group. Thus, the context out of which the variables are drawn and which may be highly unique for each man is discarded as "the chaff," with only the features they share in common as "the wheat." It is necessary for us to do this in order to compare the stereotypes of the scientist with these men's actual personality characteristics. Stereotypes by definition are generalized variables which have been drawn from the multiplicity of individual circumstance and characteristic that describe the personal case and can be applied to members of the group. Therefore in order to evaluate their accuracy, it is necessary for us to compare the same kind of generalized common denominators found in the group by empirical study with the characteristics emerging in the stereotypes.

In order to give some idea of the range of individual difference out of which the common personality variables have grown, I should like to present a number of clinically oriented descriptions of these men. These précis of their personality pictures have been drawn from their test protocols. These test analyses were also done blindly, and were written as if they were parts of case studies in a clinical setting. The test protocols presented below were chosen at random, and they sample ten members of the group.

Customarily in such reports the psychologist describes the intellectual functioning of the individual, relates this functioning to capacity, describes the emotional reactions and motivations of the person, shows how these seem to be derived from his existing conflicts, and how they are all integrated into the over-all personality functioning. Thus, the précis reveal information about a person that may not be immediately and obviously related to functioning, although highly relevant to it.

As will be evident, this is true in the case of the scientists, too, for the primary data in the descriptions of personality refer to inner psychodynamics, characteristic emotional reactions, the kinds of conflicts they have, and the personality styles they have built up. In some scientists this kind of information may appear to contradict his behavior as a scientist and the attitudes and values he may espouse. However, in other researchers, attitudes and overt behavior may be more overtly reflective of inner dynamics. In still others, scientific status and the role adopted overlay and protect more individually oriented styles of behavior. Whereas in some men this may be a consciously acquired defense, in others it is a separation between inner dynamic and outer behavior that is outside awareness.

Such information about how psychological continuity within an individual is affected is one of the major contributions of the projective tests. Because they provide a well-rounded picture of the personality, they emphasize how different aspects of behavior are wedded into an integrated whole. From this, one can predict with some degree of confidence how the individual might operate in any specific situation or under concrete circumstances. Some speculations on this level are reported in the data that follow. However, one limitation of the projective tests must be recognized: because they depend so heavily on inner fantasies, the tests tap this aspect of an individual's psychological makeup more effectively than they do his other resources and assets. As a result, a person's comfort with fantasy and his ease in using it often influences the test impressions. A man who is oriented toward reality in his thinking and is hesitant about indulging in fantasy, for example, may be handicapped on this material, appearing more constricted than he is. The tests' reliance on fantasy also encourages the more disturbed and conflictual material within an individual to be brought to the fore, often at the expense of the less disturbed areas. Therefore it is necessary to remember in reading the data that many of the behavioral features or characteristics that are revealed are not necessarily neurotic merely because they appear to be motivated by drives and emotions that are either distorted from their original aims, or incorporated in the personality in idiosyncratic ways, or distended so that a smooth and evenly balanced picture of functioning does not result. The range of individual variability among "normal" personality pictures is still unknown; but it is likely that in every classification of a "normal" group, some of the same discrepancies from the hypothesized "ideal" or "average" and some of the same conflicts and tensions that appear in this group are unmistakably present.

Subject 1, Age Thirty-three Years

This is a serious, intelligent man who has carefully carved out a "good" and "pure" characterological adjustment for

71

himself. This has been done by adopting a behavior pattern in which there is a massive reaction formation coloring a passive-aggressive personality picture. This man appears as a basically guilt-ridden, unhappy individual who has taken all his past actions and fantasies to heart, and who has decided that he can only bear these by becoming by contrast a good and upstanding person. Thus, he has taken on a behavior pattern that has many positively valued ego features —devotion, dedication to hard tasks, carrying heavy burdens on his shoulders, closing his eyes to "the devil." As a result, he lives in a highly formalized and highly moral way. His aspirations are noble, he is disdainful of "barbarities" in everyday life, and also shuns the earthly pleasures, preferring for himself a more ascetic and more emotionally pared-down existence.

In his work he scorns performance for the sake of applause or personal gain. He takes care never to show conceit for whatever successes he has and he actually feels that only "true" scientific progress can come when scientific men sever their ties to all kinds of other motives that might contaminate their true dedication. He enjoys the mysteries of science and religion, and uses both of these to keep him diverted and defended against all pulls in more impure directions.

This kind of picture has been adopted out of strong guilts and anxieties that seem to have arisen from tumultuous emotional conflicts. This man either was, or fantasied himself, a youngster who was easily led into a life which was dominated by instinctual gratifications. These earlier conflicts, pushed into the background, even now remain sufficiently close to consciousness to be revealed in the tests. He sees himself basically as a hostile person who expresses a great deal of aggressive tension in what acting out he would do were he to let himself go. In fantasy he identifies himself as a vigorous "dandy" who could feel exhilaration and relief were he to let himself go.

There is little gradation in his feelings or in his activities. He is either overly sensitive and highly labile in his feelings, developing very sensuous childlike attachments (as he did with his mother), or his emotional response is cold, icy, and formalized and he denies that feelings really exist. Similarly, sexuality is either uncontrolled, reckless, and impetuously engaged in, or everything is viewed with an asexual eye. Because he values control, self-sacrifice, and foregoing personal gratifications as attributes of maturity, these values determine his present activities, and he emerges, in the closing of his eyes to everything sexual or aggressive, in his words, as a "featureless and almost unrecognized personality."

In this quest for maturity this man has disassociated himself from his parents, attempting to rise above them because he feels that both parents are too interested in earthly things and are therefore "dangerous." The mother is seen as wanting to hold on to him as a little boy and he still resents her provocation toward this passivity. He openly dislikes his father as a castrated, droopy, and moth-eaten creature. In trying to separate himself from both as sources of identification he has emerged with a somewhat artificial, conventionalized behavior pattern for himself. Interestingly enough, in some ways he has succeeded in "castrating" himself, thus carrying out his worst fears, albeit in an intellectualized way.

Subject 2, Age Forty-three Years

This psychological picture is a mixed neurotic one, in which both obsessive compulsive and hysterical features are present in a humorous and fanciful man. He is obviously a person of superior capabilities who shows a lot of enjoyment in seeing things in unusual and even preposterous ways. He is quite stimulated by the challenges which enable him to use his imagination; and in these makes instantaneous judgments which amuse and interest him very much. He is seldom afraid of being out on a limb but instead "frolics" intellectually in this way. Because of his great openness in fantasy it is evident that a wish to retreat from the emotional environment which for him is quite a terrifying and dangerous spot motivates some of this intellectual play. Under severe emotional stress he retreats into a pedantic, ordered kind of thinking.

In many ways he is an aggressive and frustrated man, but these qualities are expressed so uniquely that he is probably quite creative in his work. He alternates between feeling that he is a dullard, like an undergraduate, "a fat man with a small brain"; and that he is potentially a creative and inventive fellow. At times these two aspects clash with each other so sharply that he feels like a dissociated personality split down the middle, and this stimulates considerable anxiety in him. Some of his anxiety is handled by acting like a moral stuffed shirt—and this front also is used to hide some of the infantile pulls he feels himself prey to— or he frequently will retreat and hide his nose in the sand, thus cutting off any threat of letting too much aggression out.

He is probably quite severe as a teacher. All his libido goes into enjoying his aggressive competition and very little into love, sex, or anything else. Instead he uses science as his battleground to act out repeatedly the tensions within him. Some self-destructive tendencies come out in his behavior which result in curbing his really strong ambitions and desires.

This man seems to have disliked a cold and abominable father and unconsciously sees all his intellectual victories as a way of showing up the father. In fact, this battle against the father goes on in fantasy in various inventive and highly imaginative ways. The mother is more identified with intellectual ambitions. He feels she wants him as a prodigy and for this he has renounced greater gains in other fields. He is filled occasionally with the fantasy of greatness but because success is so often followed by a need to fail, there is a question of whether he will ever let himself go sufficiently to bring his talents to real fruition.

74

Subject 3, Age Forty-three Years

This is an obsessive compulsive character development in a duty-bound individual. This man presents an interesting picture of a "self-made man." Actually he is a strikingly isolated person who, because few of his early ties were positive, was determined that he had to make his own way. In a kind of defensive manner, he built up the notion that he was a capable and rare person scientifically and that he had little else to offer, and therefore he has put all his eggs in one basket.

Basically, he is a quick-thinking, alert, but not particularly gifted person. He tries to be precise, to make decisions quickly, and to know what there is to know. Actually, however, he is fearful of ambiguity, feels that it holds a lot of dangers, and this has driven him for self-protective purposes to learning everything he can about the things that hold interest for him.

To this man everything that is not related to work is distraction. Everything that is pleasurable, sexual, or emotional generally conflicts with work, and although occasionally he succumbs to these, this is unusual and there is no question that what comes out in other spheres remains isolated and unintegrated into his work experiences. Sexuality, because it is unpredictable and unorganized, seems jarring and unexciting. One can see why he has assumed the character he has, because his parental relationships, which set the stage for later relationships, remain without much feeling. He feels the mother saw him as a decorative object; that he was no more than anything else that she was interested in for its exhibitionistic value. Father is seen as somebody who got away from difficulties, who was eager to flee on whatever grounds he could.

Actually, there is a lot of softness and gentleness in him. However, even his needs to be taken care of are all denied and pushed into the background, in the duty-bound, rigorous manner that he has adopted, because these characteristics are ego-alien to the conception of himself that he

75

enjoys. It is interesting that because he feels that he has pulled himself up by his bootstraps, now he feels he can be "broken down" in the same way. Therefore, he keeps his nose to the grindstone, allows little distraction and in this way keeps himself out of trouble. Here is a case of a man who developed excellent resources out of sheer frustration and now carries on in the highly stylized way that he thinks scientists should.

Subject 4, Age Thirty-six Years

This is a narcissistic character development in an ambitious, productive man who is eager for accomplishment and commendation. Though he is not a particularly creative or unusual thinker, he keeps at his task until actually achieving distinguished performance by the sheer hammering out of material. When he really lets himself go one can see that he is driven by intense, pent-up feelings of aggression which compulsively push him into productivity. These stem from feelings of neglect and frustration in the subject's early life but also represent his way of keeping his aggressive tensions fairly constructively used and well directed.

He is an interesting man because he is so many-faceted in personality development and is not hesitant to let these many sides come out. His own freedom in letting himself out without undue anxiety is matched by his openness to stimuli from the environment; and while his reactions are not always unusual to begin with, because he keeps "pounding away" he finally does get to the point where he often produces different and original responses. He vacillates in personality between being a rigid and controlled individual and one with strong affects and sensuous reactions. He has not much compunction about the latter aspects of his personality and even recognizes this kind of duality characterizing many aspects of his personality development with interest. While making a superficially adequate heterosexual adjustment, he recognizes that often for him women are frigid, offering little sensuous excitement and that he is strongly pulled toward other interests. This individual has no strong involvements with others. Essentially, his are more rapid-fire, immediate, and impulsive involvements that are narcissistically determined, than they are strong lasting attachments. These attitudes are derived from a fragmented but important relationship with the mother, whom he saw as a cold but protective kind of woman. Some of his identification elements have been taken over into this feeling about himself. The father figure seems to have left little mark on him.

Because of the strong narcissistic flavor dominating his activity, this man feels himself somewhat of a "rat" without any sensitivity. While these kinds of feelings lead to occasional depression, they do not stay with him too long and instead drive him on to get relief by plunging further into intellectual activity. There is no attempt on his part to deny the press of sexual or emotional conflict but instead he uses these conflicts as motivations and impetus for harder work activity.

Subject 5, Age Thirty-eight Years

This is a personality picture of an "overadjusted" man. He displays the characterological development of a well-adapted person with good inner resources which he uses minimally but in highly appropriate ways. Essentially he responds with a good sense of tact and considered judgment, is rational and detailed in his approach to stimuli, but the results are strikingly minimal in terms of his potential. This man shows a rich fantasy development and uses his excellent intellectual resources with selectivity and discrimination, but restricts them in such a cautious and overly considered way that one appreciates that he is using only a fraction of his potential.

This man is flexible, has a "light touch," and is certainly interested in responding in differentiated ways. Yet his need to be appropriate is so marked that it inhibits him from producing anything really unique. He gives the feeling of a man who wants to submerge himself into situations which cause him little anxiety and he puts considerable effort into deciding what situations he can respond to appropriately without suffering any anguish.

His limited aspirations are derived from a number of sources: First, his feeling that his psychological equilibrium might totter were he to do more than he could easily handle; second, his poor tolerance for the anxiety that more ambiguous situations seem to engender in him; third, his desire to restrict all his conflicts to situations he knows about. For him, decisions about what to do in the light of obligations to others, for example, involve a big morality issue. He is bothered by his responsibilities, and often wishes he could flee from them.

He experiences very great pleasure in enjoyment of what is. In fact he enjoys the present to such an extent that it suggests there must be something else behind his unusual pleasure. The tests show how this enjoyment of today comes from severe anxieties about being hurt which he generally keeps repressed. Underneath his good front, he feels that he is an inadequate figure who might not always be able to foresee everything, and who is afraid that things may get out of his control. Also, he knows men are frequently ridiculous and his fears that he will be laughed at prevent him from trying to do anything he is not able to do perfectly. As a result, his performance tends to be on the dull, even pedantic side, although he has a great potential for imagination and originality.

Occasionally aggressions come out in his behavior, but for the most part they are kept back, as are most of his feelings. Only in the framework of fantasy is the breadth and depth of emotion revealed. Some hostility toward women is present, and would seem to stem from a rather frigid kind of relationship with the mother; part of his not wanting to extend himself professionally also represents a form of rebellion toward her. Yet, more important are his fears that his talents would be robbed were he to expose them, and that his resources could readily be taken advantage of. In fact, this is such a prevalent theme in his test material that it hints of a slight guarded flavor in his personality makeup. He must always be the one to make decisions, and yet he sets decisions up in such a way that a choice can be readily made even before the conflict is spelled out.

Subject 6, Age Forty Years

This is an obsessive compulsive personality picture with schizoid underpinnings, in an extremely passive man. Although he puts considerable effort into productivity, his great passivity and masochism direct his energies mainly toward finding spots in which dependent longings can be gratified. This is his most dedicated effort, in a way, and it is done with such neatness, care, and rationality that he becomes an extremely effective person—but in single areas alone. Although superficially outgoing and industrious, he is withdrawn and ridden by fantasies which have a repetitious and compulsive flavor.

He is gifted but shows his talents in a quiet and unassuming way. The unassumingness is part of his trouble, and seems to stem from two sources: first, a fear of being aggressive, which arises from an internalization of a harsh and critical superego; second, a feeling of being incapable of meeting what eventualities might come his way.

This last aspect of his self-image stems from his identification with a father who, although physically big and powerful, was extremely passive and dependent. The son seems to have assimilated into his conception of himself this discrepancy between apparent potential power and actual power that he saw in his father. He feels that he is not too strong intellectually and therefore prefers to circumscribe the things he attempts. He is regarded as a nice person who treads delicately and does not engender antagonisms in others.

Because of this need to do what is expected and proper, he makes some limited—but quite unspontaneous—gestures to relate emotionally. He is actually little interested in

79

others except as sources of nurturance. Otherwise, he considers people stiff and "uncivilized." In heterosexual relationships people appear to him to be merely thrown together, and he tries to keep interactions from clashing. He allows other people's motivations to subordinate his, is very self-effacing, and will accept doing what he feels is distasteful in order to keep conflicts from arising. He is careful to shut out any resentments.

He has fantasies of being a great man and these dreams plague him, but he neatly isolates them from whatever he does in reality.

Subject 7, Age Thirty-nine Years

This is a narcissistic character picture in a guilt-ridden man with a low anxiety tolerance. He is flamboyant and rambunctious, impatient, critical, and intolerant. He has energy and a lot of intellectual push which at this moment seems to be bottled up so that he is left with feelings of guilt and frustration over not performing. He is a man who thinks quickly and sizes up situations rapidly, but if these do not immediately jell into something that makes sense for him he gets very disturbed and projects the blame onto the material, and then dismisses it. Actually, he is constantly preoccupied with his performance. His being very critical of the test material is only one form which his criticism takes. He is also such a harsh and intolerant taskmaster toward himself that he would make mincemeat of himself and his abilities, were at least not some of his criticism directed outwardly.

This man strives to make something ambiguous into something concrete and tangible; something where alternatives are sufficiently limited to suggest a structure for him. In this he seeks discipline from the outside where he lacks it internally. He becomes carping, nagging, crying out at the world in a plea for more structure and more organization; and yet much of this leaves him dissatisfied because he rejects the obvious and conventional as too phony and too pat.

This same overreaction characterizes his emotional behavior. He vacillates between thinking that nothing is meaningful, stable or satisfying, and engaging in behavior in which he compulsively and desperately looks for stability in meaning and relationships. He feels that he has been beaten by life because he has so few gratifications, but this is partly because his need for these is intense, demanding, immediate. He seems readily given to rages in the face of disappointment and therefore often cuts off the persons who could give him some of the stability that he demands.

This man has leaned heavily on his father for the security and discipline he needed; and now with the father gone he feels that he has not internalized controls sufficiently to keep him on an even keel and working maturely. He feels he has not quite come to fruition, and much as he extols the father for at least setting the stages, at the same time he is very hostile toward him for being the seat of these tremendous and overwhelming self-demands. He saw his mother as a narcissistic self-centered person with little time for him; and now in his own behavior the scientist constantly reaches out for women who will nurture him, pick him up, and give him the kind of dependency gratification that he needs. Therefore, it is likely that he engages in some acting out of personal needs. He is afraid to be "hooked" by a woman because he knows how great his need for women is; consequently, he always manages to alienate them.

This man is dramatic and exhibitionistic even in his remorse. He is really troubled and conscience stricken, even desperate at times, but because there is so much lack of control and bluster in this, his own unhappiness is likely to be beclouded by the antagonisms he provokes.

Subject 8, Age Thirty-seven Years

This is a very dignified, well-controlled, esthetic man. He presents a picture of a long-standing personality adjustment in which denial, repression, and isolation have been prominent: so much so that he operates in a highly stylized, nonconflictful way in which little spontaneity comes out. He appears to be a studied intellectual who has taken pride in the precise way his intellectual endeavors are carried out. Preferring things which raise no anxiety or conflicts within him, he perceives things inevitably as pleasant and undisturbing, and thus in some way maintains the same kind of intellectual objectivity and uninvolvement in whatever task he sets out to do. Verbalizations are careful almost to the point of preciousness; and he puts considerable effort into carving out for himself those areas of response in which his characteristic ways of handling things will be at a premium. Therefore one is struck by the fact that often he ignores the obvious and instead focuses on one aspect of a problem which is easy for him and around which he becomes quite imaginative. Therefore he is unlikely to be much of a generalist in science, but instead is more interested in the kind of details which are not fraught with the ambiguity that might lead to anxiety.

Emotional responses in this man tend to be superficial and forced. It is likely that all object relations are shallow, if they exist at all. Any strong interpersonal involvement is seen as tragic, and therefore he shies away from any intense relationship quite unwittingly. This role that he has cut out for himself stems from his mother's need to treat him as a "kewpie doll" because of her own immaturity and limitations. He remains in his psychosexual role as a little boy who has everything in place and who will have no truck with anything that is displaced and which he would thus consider "unfortunate." He sees his father as evil, and therefore does not want to be like him. Since he could not tolerate such feelings in himself, the father is cut out of his emotional consciousness, and only occasional momentary thoughts of him come out. He is openly hostile to his parents and there are no feelings for them which are acceptable. This has led into a limited psychological development which his esthetic cultured leanings tend to hide.

This man looks at the world from the gaze of a "gentleman," and work for him is a way of thinking about things which would disturb him if he looked at them without the rosy glasses that science provides. He sees anything to do with the body as unclean and unfortunate, but if his biological interests are sufficiently masked in an intellectual way, he can even enjoy the satisfactions that come from his achievements in this field.

Subject 9, Age Fifty-nine Years

This personality picture is of a passive and self-effacing individual who is given to the development of somatization symptoms under stress. He is a withdrawn and depressed man who feels himself to be a "dried-out" and empty person, though superficially this picture is covered over by his adopting a kindly compromising, overly tolerant manner. He maintains a front of being unusually gentle and quiet, but this rather than being a behavior pattern that he has adopted by choice turns out to be a massive defensive reaction against any show of independent action. In his passivity he hides the fact that he is not a particularly vital or resourceful person—but is instead a man who withdraws from anything which demands initiative or assertiveness. Through the maintenance of a submissive position, he actually permits himself to be hamstrung by responsibility and obligations which prevent him from being put into positions in which he would have to assume a strongly authoritative or assertive role. While this defense seems to convince outsiders, Dr. X actually feels that he has little wherewithal for productiveness at this age, and in fact he wonders if he has not always been a rather nondescript, ineffective figure both intellectually and personally.

He is so overcautious and tentative in his expression that he has little freedom for fantasy or spontaneity. Instead he clings to the obvious in his thinking and avoids being recognized for this because he does not allow himself to get pinned down or put on the spot. He constantly feels himself in danger of being exposed, and so is overly concerned about personal privacy. And while he identifies with groups which fight to maintain individual liberties, his own activities on this behalf stem from his needs to keep hidden what he thinks are his personal weaknesses.

He sees the father figure, by contrast to himself, as courageous and unafraid. He has tried to identify himself in his external roles with the father but actually has managed to get himself into so many situations that tie him down and hamstring him, that he really is almost never forced to test this kind of courage. He is very submissive to women because he needs their approval very much and so has given up most impulsive activities on which they might frown. He blames women for keeping him from doing what he wants but he does not recognize that in letting women make "sacrifices" for him he thus obligates himself to them. Dr. X is struck by the lack of differentiation in men's and women's roles and while he feels very threatened by women who have taken over what he thought was his position, he does not permit any resentment or aggression toward them to come out directly.

It is only through his work that he permits any enjoyment for enjoyment's sake; but in this area his functioning is so circumscribed that one would predict that he ventures into few areas where "angels fear to tread."

Subject 10, Age Forty-five Years

This man presents a picture of a passive-aggressive character development in which obsessive compulsive features are prominent. The psychological picture is that of an intelligent and capable man who drives himself in intellectual work despite his ambivalence about work and competition. He is a man with strong dependency needs, strong wishes to be taken care of and protected, and strong wishes to retreat from competition. Yet he cannot allow himself to give way to these dependency needs because for him, weakness and inadequacy are tied up with these longed-for fantasies. Instead he defends himself against them by working hard and compulsively, despite his wishes to the contrary. His strong work effort is now reinforced by pressing status and prestige needs. He is very much driven by the fact that his mother still takes pride in his intellectual achievements, even though his prowess has in certain ways separated him from the family.

Actually, this is a man who often steps into danger and difficulties because he is so afraid that people will be really aggressive to him. He is basically a fearful, easily menaced person, and in an effort to reassure himself, will often provoke aggressions which he knows he can handle. He sees himself as the victim, the one who is always picked on by others—not appreciative of his own role in creating this situation.

He is really a man who would like to be an "ostrich," a feeling that stems from identification with the father toward whom he feels a strong emotional tie, although the father is ambivalently seen as a "skeleton in a fur coat." The patient's own image of himself gives evidence of this ambivalence; alternately attributing ability and power to himself and feeling that he is incomplete, unable to do anything which makes him call for extra help from others to bolster himself.

This kind of dual conception even pervades his personal relationships. Here too, he fantasies and wishes that he were like a "lower-status" person who could be rough and tough with women, something he could never be. He is very dependent on women, especially on his wife. He does with women what he does with colleagues to show his aggression—he denigrates their work or their strength, calls them foolish, but obviously knows that some of this is a bluff in which he hides his need for them.

This man tends to renounce the things he enjoys doing, by saying that duty is first, and that he must contribute to the world. Yet, this is at least partly a rationalization for not having resolved problems around work and for dutiful obedience to authority figures.

85

The results drawn from the quantitative analysis of the experimental data indicate that the individual differences within the group are greater than the common denominators. None of the hypotheses that refer to particular behavior patterns or kinds of conflicts proved to be successful in identifying the group. For example, the results indicate that the scientist does not have one specific kind of personality structure defined by the psychosexual level to which his psychological development has progressed; nor is there a predominance of one major kind of defense structure. No hypotheses suggesting any particular emotional constellation as extremely pertinent were tenable: the scientist is not given particularly to changes of mood; he is not particularly passive, submissive or dependent; he does not shy away from strong interpersonal relationships; the scientist is not bisexual, nor is he ridden by unusually strong ambivalent conflicts. The generalization that scientists are characterized by particular kinds of conflicts over sexuality, authority, or performance does not stand up to experimental test. Rather, the personality pictures are varied and show that the men in this vocation have chosen science to satisfy diverse needs and have found diverse satisfactions. In fact, none of the personality characteristics that emerge as common denominators is significant for one diagnostic category as compared to all the others. They can be considered common to a number of personality pictures, and even find expression within these personality pictures in a number of ways.

I shall first list the emotional and motivational variables that stood up to experimental test, and then I shall discuss how these contribute to the scientist's functioning as a researcher.

The results indicate that (1) the scientist has strong emotional leanings to intellectual activity; (2) he is independent in his thought and actions, and does not mimic others; (3) he is challenged by frustration and anxiety-producing situations; (4) curiosity is likely to be a major determinant in his work; (5) strong ego involvement and conflict are expressed in work; (6) he does not use parental ideals to set up his own goals; (7) he shows a strong capacity for sensual gratification; (8) he is motivated by a desire to master or interpret natural forces or reality; (9) he is sensitive to the moods and feelings of others; (10) he is sensitive to his internal environment, needs, wishes, desires; (11) he values work primarily as permitting expression of inner personality.

These individual variables cluster around a few main trends; I shall focus on these in discussing the role such personality variables play in scientific performance.

❦ Emotional Investment in Intellectual Activities

THE SCIENTISTS are all excellently endowed with intellectual capacities. They range in intellectual level from high average to very superior.[1] This means that beginning with their earliest days they were probably able to manipulate certain kinds of things, ideas, and people in their environment with facility; they were probably able to explore and cope with their world and manage it with superior skills and modes of response. These abilities, however, even tied as they are to normal maturation, are not developed automatically in childhood; they must be learned. The fact that these skills have become "second nature" today indicates how much satisfaction and pleasure the men must have derived from the uses of their resources.

The findings show that the scientist has immersed himself deeply in intellectual interests and activities. Much of his self-realization as an adult is derived from the fact that he is doing work that not only places a premium on the intellect but is often an exciting, intellectual pursuit. His superior mental capacities and his curiosity propel him to look for work that will make use of his resources. We can speculate that, from the beginning of their intellectual development, these men enjoyed putting their wits to different problems and situations, and found both conscious and unconscious gratifications in their investment in intellectual pursuits.

Emotional investment in something is not likely to be an all-or-none process, or dependent on a one-shot experience. It proceeds with trial and error, with ambivalence and unevenness, until the final anchoring of certain interests and pursuits becomes one's consistent pattern of satisfactions. The regularity, consistency, and stability of the satisfiers that one uses make it possible to describe a person's adult identity in terms of the myriad ways in which he has invested himself. These can be hierarchically ordered to show how expenditures of time, energy, and emotions have contributed to forming certain aspects of identity.

In the interviews, the scientists could only speculate retrospectively about the experiences that had made intellectual activities their outlets for personal resources. Some mentioned how intellectual things had never lost for them the character of play, with its experimental possibilities, its stimulus to fantasy and daydreaming, its imaginative spans with no thought of product.[2] They felt that this jumping off into the unknown was a unique pleasure, and many traced its precursors to their very early days. One theoretical chemist described it this way:

> I think my liking for science began so early, it was innate. I have always enjoyed ordering phenomena. It pleased me very much to have what might be called an understanding of the world. Every time I found some new—to me, new—explanation of phenomena, I was pleased. I remember when I was quite young, I looked through an umbrella at a distant

arc light, and saw the spectra in different colors—four out [gesturing] like this, and then the intermediate ones coming in at 45° angles in between the four principal spectra—and I wondered what caused this. Then, when I learned about deflection by cross-grading—much later, of course—I was pleased that I understood.

The developmental histories of our scientists in the previous chapter have hinted at the diversity of sources that fed the investment in the intellectual. Its expression also emerges in many ways. Most directly, of course, it is channeled into scientific work, though it determines leisure interests as well. Two men, for example, avidly study and read in the histories of medicine and science. Another spends half his time writing books that generalize the application of scientific developments for the social and political welfare of mankind. A few read extensively in the fields of political history, biography, or light fiction; two see beating the stock market as the greatest problem-solving game; and one chemist admits waiting anxiously until new appliances in his house break down, so that he can have the opportunity of seeing how they work.

The phrase "emotional investment" may not suggest the intense nature of intellectual experiences. These activities are described by such adjectives as "thrilling," "intimate," "completely possessing," and the long hours, the dedication, the slavish devotion—which are part of what LaFarge has called the "emotions of science"—are only the external manifestations of the almost inexpressible affective content. Here is the way one man tells of the thrills that science provides:

I think the biggest thrills I've had in my life, the most satisfying things I've ever done, are the few little discoveries I've made. This is a satisfaction of a kind I've never experienced in any other respect. I mean, if I invested one thousand

89

dollars in a stock, and it appreciated fivefold in a month, this would be a kind of satisfaction, but nothing compared to this other kind of satisfaction. If I made a million dollars tomorrow, certainly I'd feel good, but it would be nothing compared to the several new things I've come up with. They were kind of accidents in a way; but the point is that these particular things—like the first time E. and I transplanted an eye on a fly—were at the time spectacular technical achievements. It turned out that this is easy now—anybody can do it—but the first time was hard. When we did it, we didn't know why we were doing it, so we went down to a café and sat for half a day, saying, "Can we do it again?" And, secondly, "What the hell will we do with it if we can?" After we did it, we then thought of something that we could do with it, and it turned out we were pretty lucky. Well, the half-day in the café thinking about it—this was a real satisfaction and thrill, better than any other kind of thrill I've ever had. When we took the next step and found we could use it for something we found a pretty spectacular result—but that's a second step.

I think this is one factor that's important in the development of scientists—the satisfaction of an achievement that you know is an achievement. I would say that perhaps in my own case it's the most important thing I ever experienced and that ever influenced me. If you take the people in the United States classified as scientists—I don't know how many hundreds of thousands there are—a large number of these, probably 99.9 per cent, or maybe it's 99 per cent, have never experienced the thrill of really doing something they know is important, that they can just sense "this is it!" You can do lots of things you can publish papers on, if you're any good in science, but that isn't the real thing. That has to be done, it's a contribution, and so forth; but once in a while you make this decisive step that you know is going to change the future of science, and I think it's a kind of thrill that nothing else can equal. If a bright student can experience this, you can't stop him; if he experiences it once, he wants to do it again.

Such satisfactions cannot fail to keep emotional investment in intellectual activities fresh and constantly revital-
ized. And only occasionally does one become aware of some
of the unhappy implications of such enthusiasms. This same
biologist continues:

> Of course, if you make an achievement like that too early—
> well, it can be a little depressing. Take, for example, the
> discouragement that the fellow faces who invented this
> model on my desk. It is the most significant achievement of
> biology in the present century, I think. He did this at
> twenty-six. He's a bright guy and an independent one. His
> college record was spotty because if he didn't like a subject,
> "to hell with it." If he liked it, he was an A student. He's
> smart enough to know that what he has done is so important
> he can't do it again, and this is discouraging because he did
> this when he was only twenty-six, and everybody says, "He's
> terrific! He's one of the brightest guys in the world!" So
> they're all going to say, "He ought to do another thing like
> that." He knows that in a lifetime his chance of doing this
> again—or the equivalent—is almost zero, so he's going to
> be a little depressed by this, isn't he?

However, because emotional investment in intellectual
activities is so constantly refired by the curiosity drive, few
scientists are really concerned with such consequences. Curiosity may direct the progress from one aspect of an experiment to the other, may more abstractly stimulate the desire
to find ways of integrating internal experiences with those
in the external world, and may direct the compelling scientific need to master the natural forces of reality. Psychologists once thought that all drives—organic as well as exploratory or manipulative—produce tension within us until they
are somehow met or relieved, and that, once met, the tensions abate and the experience of pleasure follows. Now they
realize that at times the greatest pleasures may be derived

91

from the tension itself, at least until it reaches the point where it becomes more disruptive than enjoyable. The curiosity drive itself has been described this way; the satisfactions accruing during the building up actually matching and even surpassing the denouement, which becomes a sort of anticlimax. A theoretical physicist has described this very vividly:

> I don't know why I keep looking for the big problems. I suppose one of the things is curiosity. I think I'd be dishonest to say that it was the only reason. In a way, I really don't know why I do it, but I suppose I can answer you to some extent when I describe what goes on within me. When I'm not working on something big, I generally have a lowish feeling. During this period, I'm not unhappy in any general low sense, just negative. I'm not getting the bang out of doing something that I get in going to a dance or playing drums. It's something I want to do. Life's still interesting, exciting; I make trips, do different things—teach, see my students—but it doesn't have that extra thing which is the great pleasure. In addition, there's the mild feeling that I'm worn out or burned out, and this is the end of my career. Or I've some feelings of responsibility I wish I could get rid of, that I ought to be doing something. It drives you into a locked position where you just can't do anything right.
>
> During the war, there wasn't any big problem that I was working on, even though it was at the time of the atomic bomb. There were a number of relatively easy problems in succession, so that there were tremendous numbers of little successes. We had a different kind of problem, and there was a great pressure for the work. The reason the problems were easier was that nobody had worked on them before. They weren't the kind of problems that had been unsolved because nobody could solve them; they were unsolved because they hadn't been attacked. If problems have been worked on, and nobody has solved them, then you've got difficulty. These are the kind of problems I like to work on. I'm not one who could ever be satisfied with a large

number of small problems. They just somehow don't drive my curiosity enough. But it's the big problems that excite you. Maybe I got two or three in ten years, but they're so dramatic, so much fun, that when you get them, it's worth it. It's like hunting lions, not rabbits: you don't get many lions, but if you do get a lion, you feel better. Then you can go off and shoot rabbits more easily.

With so much of the scientist's feeling of self tied up in his work, it is not surprising to find that this becomes the stage at which the passions get spent and the gamut of emotions—at other times concealed—revealed. Scientific work is no impersonal, cut-and-dried matter, yet the rationality of scientific methods is frequently confused with the internal experiences and feelings of scientists.[3]

A close look at the interests of the few men who show tremendous zest and enthusiasm for a diversity of things showed me that these expansive pursuits can all be related to scientific activity or the promotion of scientific sensibilities. All their interests are approached with the same orientation and worked at with the same precision and discipline. Few interests are pursued for nonscientific reasons, and even these interests that seem to be pursued for other reasons often turn out to enhance or whet the appetite for the activities which soon follow. Noontime handball is acceptable only when it comes after some hours of work and will be followed by more work. It is, or at least it is rationalized as, "the physical pause that mentally refreshes."

❧ Emotional Constriction and Control

THIS LEADS US to the second major common denominator in personality: emotional constriction and control. Constriction does not mean the lessened intensity of emotion, but rather the narrowness of the emotional experience, the channelized ways of expression, the restricted and controlled ways of response. It is contrasted with emotional lability, overreactivity, fluidity in response. Emotional expression is not undiversified or completely unspontaneous; it is restricted in the ways it gets expressed, and often comes out more openly in fantasy than in direct relationships.

Emotional withdrawal, isolation, and loneliness are words which appear frequently in the stereotyped concept of a scientist's personality. According to this empirical study, this seems to be an incorrect conception. It apparently has been derived largely from the fact that the scientist is often in an isolated setting, and engaged in solitary work. These findings support Lionel Trilling's contention that the major representation of the creative person as being alienated or isolated stems partly from the nature of his work and partly from the uniqueness and originality that make his product different from others. Trilling feels that this is one reason why creative persons' life histories are often conceived of as being long experiences of rejection and misunderstanding.

The picture of the scientists emerging from the psychological tests is not one of withdrawal, as we know it clinically, or of a differentiated, elaborated response to varied stimuli, but one in which emotional expression finds outlets in limited areas. There is no breadth of emotional involvement, nor are intense relationships with people frequent; those that exist are usually with other persons who share work interests and scientific experiences.

Since the main enthusiasms are bound up in what is, to a greater or lesser extent, solitary work, passions may propel work in a way that otherwise would not be possible. They may serve also to sustain these men during the tedious hours, the routine tasks, and the times of failure. How work sustains emotions and how, on the other hand, emotions sustain work, is not simple to sort out; we know this from the way the scientists describe their feelings during periods of strong work power and during unproductive times. None describes feelings of loneliness when he works day and night alone on something urgent. Loneliness is more likely to be the outcome of detachment and aloofness from people during an unproductive period. The comfort derived from work and the closeness to oneself and one's resources experienced during work seem to provide a cloak that insulates the scientist from the emotional distance existing in nonwork situations.

There seems to be almost no activity for the scientist that offers as much gratification as science; it is no wonder that both other activities and activities with others are pale by contrast. The tests indicate that this is an overdetermined reaction, because the scientist feels that he knows and can trust his own personal resources, but he has doubts about relying on others and trusting them.

The biographical information shows that, in general, adult relationships have been stable. There is a minimal amount of internal churning about the troubles and unhappinesses of others or of themselves. For the most part, the scientists seem fairly happy and satisfactorily adjusted, in the sense of not having too much open conflict. They demand much less support from relationships outside of work, and much less of their sense of personal identity comes from their other roles. I was struck, for example, by the fact that family problems, and even some very severe psychological disorders in children and wives, arouse relatively little conflict in these scientists as husbands and fathers—not comparable to the degree that work problems arouse. The migraine headaches come after committee meetings and not after fights with the wife. The affect seems to be siphoned into work to such a degree that everything else seems to have much less impact, and scarcely any other aspect of life experience can compete successfully for the emotional involvement of these men. In a peculiarly circular way, the emotional overinvestment in work seems to reinforce the psychological conditions which originally might have given rise to it, and this, then, turns back to insulate the scientist from being too disturbed by human conflict in other areas.

If the channeling of the emotion into limited areas were really the same as withdrawal or uninvolvement, as is described classically in the case of Willard Gibbs, for example, I think there would be much less conflict within the area of work.[4] It seems to me significant that after one chemist told of his tremendous need to be best in whatever aspect of the field he might have gone into, a colleague mentioned inadvertently that the same man actively discouraged anybody else from trying to do research in areas that he thought infringed on his province. Obviously this kind of competitiveness, with its authority orientation and concomitant narcissistic demands, is one aspect of such singular preoccupation.

This narrowness and singularity of scientific preoccupation prevents the dispersion of devotion and energy, and so propels scientific activity. Take resistance to interference or disturbance in the laboratory. Here, one is often bombarded by noises from all sides. The worker's resistance to distractions is possible only if he uses very strong isolating mechanisms. Also, scientists describe their compulsively disciplined work habits as their greatest assets, and it seems highly improbable that they could have become what they are without keeping emotional and intellectual interests in other life involvements to a minimum, and thus freeing themselves for work. Some men keep rigid schedules, with specific times allotted for specific kinds of work. One geophysicist, for example, tells how he divides his day into two parts: one in which he does research of his own, and the other in which he works for the university. He is extremely proud of his ability to shut off one thing and get started on another immediately, with almost no effort wasted in changing gears. This demands a sharp closing out of tensions and activities that could easily flow from one area into another. It ties up with what psychologists have found experimentally in the field of perception—

that the amount of distraction tolerated by an individual seems to be related to the strength of his reliance on emotional isolation as a defense mechanism.[5]

Persistence, too, is facilitated by this isolating mechanism. One scientist has worked on a problem in plant biology on and off since 1941, picking it up and returning to it again as new methods brought fresh promise for its solution. Another received a Nobel Prize for a problem he had worked on for twenty-five years. Another stows away his research ideas in a drawer so that he will not forget any of them. Each idea then becomes so much a part of him that when he later reads that someone else has picked up one of "his" ideas and "cracked it," he feels scooped, although he and his students may never have gotten around to working on it.

Judging from the results of the tests, this emotional constriction and control seems to be an ingrained feature of the personality structure of our sample of scientists. This seems to corroborate, at least partially, a line of development that was suggested in the biographical material. In the adult, after professional channels have captured the emotional energies, work seems to proceed as it does partly because there is so little effort and emotional involvement directed elsewhere. In turn, the rewarding way in which work uses this emotional constriction and control tends to reinforce it in the behavior pattern. Therefore, a personality trait that developed from conditions and propensities independent of science, seems to have found quite felicitously new and independent support because of its value in the vocational role.

❧ Anxieties and Fears

THE FOREGOING may, mistakenly, create the impression that everything in the scientist's psychology works out happily for his over-all adjustment, that he is left in a state of removed but complete bliss. It is true that his lack of free-floating anxieties and fears is striking. As a group, and with few exceptions, the scientists in our sample would be classified clinically as character types or problems rather than as neurotics merely because they show so little symptomatic anxiety and tension. This does not mean that the scientists have no anxiety; it means rather that the anxiety is bound up in the personality structure in such a way that it creates little or no consciously felt disturbance because the men have enduring, habitual ways of handling it which serve to keep it from making them uncomfortable. In other words, the scientists make relatively constant, habitual adjustments in the face of problem or conflict situations, and these keep anxiety from getting so great that it interferes with performance. Instead, as the quantitative results show, scientists are challenged by anxiety-producing situations, rather than being thrown by them.

Anxiety can be mobilized by any number of situations, as it can be derived from any number of conflicts. Some anxieties are perfectly appropriate to reality situations; others are neurotic and more related to internal conflicts. In actual manifestation, however, one may get only a hint of what these conflicts are. Often neurotic anxieties are displayed in such devious ways that they may be recognized only through understanding the symptoms within the frame of the basic personality structure. Although some psychologists feel that there are core anxieties within a personality to which others become attached, the secondary anxieties can often suggest the nature of the basic difficulties.

The psychological tests tend to reveal some of the latent fears and anxieties that have produced tension within the subjects; the tests indicate also that many of the men in this group who have conflicts expect to resolve them through scientific work. Both the nature of these conflicts and the expectations in regard to the solutions offered by work are different for each subject.

The field of science offers unlimited fantasy possibilities and scientists therefore see it as providing bountiful opportunities for resolution of disturbance. Instead of being viewed as a highly institutionalized vocation in which roles and duties are preset, science appears as a world that is easily manipulated to one's needs, and sufficiently variegated to be able to be adapted in any of the ways one wants to conceive of it. For example, a few of the group see the scientific setting as a platform on which the main dramas of life are played in scenes that are high-powered and colorful. One chemist thinks of himself as an imaginative and responsive fellow who feels that circumstances constantly threaten to blot out his sensitivity. He is aware of getting himself into situations which are unusually demanding of great creativity, and at the same time he has the hunch that despite his great ingenuity and success in handling these he is close to danger. He sees his destiny as a fighter in the big life drama in which he is the ¯maltreated victim, pitted against overwhelming forces of evil, garbed only in his scientific armor. Some of this heightened fantasy is tied up with the image of the father who died early and whom he now pictures as a "fallen hero."

For another scientist, the childhood battle with the father has been removed to the scientific battleground. While a child, he had little to do with the father, scorning him as a nonintellectual, and he attaches himself in imagination—and to some extent in fact—to one great scientist after another. His history showed that he would leave each professor after a few years, convinced that he had been exploited by him, while in reality, it looks as if he is the exploiter.

Some anxieties are related to aspirations, to doubts about achieving goals—and to some extent, these are realistic. Yet they also are found among scientists whose stature is undisputed and whose achievements have even surpassed

99

their earlier hopes. In others, anxieties express more directly underlying feelings of personal inadequacy.

One man describes how insignificant he feels as a person, an attitude which for him is emphasized through his working with the forces of nature. These forces seem to make him feel nebulous, unformed—like a jellyfish—and only because his work defines a small aspect of the world does he feel himself assuming some definite or specific shape. Another feels himself out of place in science and yet unable to break away from it, because his parents conditioned him to think that only through scientific work can manliness be achieved. This man suffers from periodic illnesses that direct attention to the helplessness he feels in scientific work, and yet at the same time they serve to release him from the tremendous pressures of the laboratory. During periods when he is functioning adequately, he tends to seek out the great authorities, hoping they will give him the support he needs. Another feels that he is second-rate, that he does not deserve any greater success than he has achieved; he conceives of scientific work as being hard and demanding, as bowing him down with responsibility and self-denial; he feels that he can establish his worth only through surviving the tremendous work stress. This man seeks out the very difficult with the regularity of a repetition compulsion, thus his testing grounds are severe.

One scientist, whose public activities are an extremely lively part of his career, considers himself "moth-eaten." For him, science is a way of pushing himself into the foreground, of being assertive, of silencing his self-doubts. His activities serve to make him appear a prodigy and at the same time to hide his lack of a fuller life. He has a number of major interests, and he has developed his "multidexterity" in part to keep him from "sticking his neck out" too far in any one direction.

This proving of one's self through scientific work as a

denial of dependency makes its appearance frequently in the psychological test pictures. Many visualize science as a way to fight the guilt and weight of loneliness brought on by awareness of dependency needs. Two scientists (both of whom feel themselves personally ugly) were raised exclusively by their mothers, since their fathers deserted them early in life. One sees scientific work as his way of pleasing the mother, for it plays out a role that she fantasied about the father, and yet this man must keep himself from being too much like the father by feeling that whatever he does in scientific work is worthless—that it is a mere "drop in the bucket" compared to what he should be or could be producing. Still another chemist's feeling of inadequacy seems related to his notion that he is odd and different from his capable sisters. Another's inadequacies are tied up with his feelings of rejection by the mother, feelings so deep-seated that despite his excellent performance in work he has to deny or mock its importance and seriousness; in fact, all scientific work receives some of his scorn. He is disdainful and disillusioned not only about what he does but also about what others do, and openly says that science serves only to insulate him, and too many others, from emotional involvement.

Many scientists seek out the "rationality" of science. Some fear their own adjustment is shaky and that, were they in a more ambiguous work situation, their own psychological balance would be threatened. A few were aware of how much their need to stick tightly to preconceived notions about science limits their work. For some, the rationality of science serves primarily to check impulsive behavior. The threats stimulated by the pressures of the irrational or uncontrolled are to some extent based upon reality, for some of these men have, at various periods in their lives, had strong pulls to "let themselves go." Yet, for others, the threats are more related to latent wishes, drives, and desires. One fears the "sensuous and animal instincts" that made his adolescence so wild and confused. Science provides him with an outer coat of refinement, as it does a scientist who describes himself as sexually promiscuous. One chemist whose early life was strikingly conventional, conforming, and carefully planned—in accordance with the demands of his very proper family in a small midwestern town—is now so troubled by his wishes to be nonconforming that he uses science to keep him safe as the conventional, conforming, proper little boy that he was; only in his fantasies do some of the emotionally charged instinctual desires make their appearance.

While some scientists primarily perceive science as rational, others see it, even with its emphasis on the structured and logical, as "irrational." One man, for example, sees his work as confronting him with the frightening and the unknown. His greatest fears are of getting in beyond his depth and not knowing when to ask for help, and of constantly finding himself out on a scientific limb. But for others work is the sanctuary, the peaceful haven, the isolated retreat where passivity can be enjoyed. More than that, it provides a way by which passivity can be regarded as most acceptable and not condemned as "laziness." One theoretical physicist sees his work not only as a surcease from the immediate present and what he considers the violences of the everyday but also as a means by which he will not have to work too hard, for he knows—or at least he rationalizes—that the great advances are not necessarily accomplished through energetic overactivity. His attitudes about this, however, contrast with those of his parents, who have persistently and naggingly tried to push him into a great deal of assertiveness and activity. He responds by feeling tired and lethargic much of the time, although he performs satisfactorily enough. Only when he moves away from his parents does he work at the rate he really enjoys, and then feels he can accomplish something. By contrast, one young chemist sees science as a way of permitting the expression of hostility and aggression in a nice, civilized way—the only way he can permit it to come out at all. He, of all the group, is most preoccupied with philosophical problems associated with science.

It is evident here that scientific research is thought of as serving apparently counterposed attitudes around aggression and passivity. I say "apparently counterposed" because one of the main contributions of psychology has been in showing that two apparently conflicting attitudes can be essentially different aspects of the same personality dimension. We know that what looks like passivity on the surface may at one and the same time be the denial of aggression and its indirect expression. One geochemist, fearing his own competitive drives—which are associated with a very tightly maintained narcissistic fantasy about his omnipotence—sees science as enabling him to dole out his aggressions systematically, and thus within his control. His work process and environment are stable and well organized—as if the built-in controls he needed were in fact merely provided by these externals. (His longing for an aristocratic family background gives us an idea about how strong his rejection of his parents is and why he has to keep his aggression so tightly under control.)

For some scientists, the two sides of the ambivalence in aggressive conflicts were more directly visible: one hard-working and very devoted chemist feels that were he to give up even to a small degree the long hours and extreme dedication to his duties, he would flee from science completely and would, therefore, be lost to it and to himself. The strength of his needs for dependency frightens him very much, and he sees work as a way of providing a substantial framework for him. His scientific work is in line not only with his parents' occupations but also with their expectations for him and for his brothers. However, although his family provides the stimulus for work, they are also his tormentors. He interprets any

103

self-protest toward what he does as an aggressive act, particularly against his mother; significantly, he qualifies any of his nonscientific hobbies as "merely other interests, not rebelling." (This attitude has an adolescent flavor—an impression made stronger by the fact that this man makes friends more easily with young girls than with women. One cannot help associating here to Lewis Carroll.)

Some men felt that choosing a field which parents could not understand was *ipso facto* rebellion; others interpreted this as independence; obviously, for most it was a little of both—perhaps stemming from the competitive relationship to the father, but ultimately in the service of personal emancipation and freedom. Only a few men were directly encouraged by a parent to go into scientific work. Many more were openly urged toward medicine which had a prestige science had not yet achieved. One subject's mother had impressed him with how superior he was to other children and had decried every relationship which was not in keeping with her notions about how such a "superior boy" should act. Science fortunately fitted into her actions, but her son unconsciously felt that her degree of overemphasis must be compensatory for some real inferiority in him. Even as an adult he feels worthless and ineffectual as a scientist, although others consider his work excellent.

The findings show that as a group scientists were not unusually bound by parental ideals in setting their goals—in fact, they had revolted against them, and were self-directed and self-disciplined in their thinking to a significant degree. These scientists tended to reject unusual imitation of, or dependency on, authority figures. Some assumed responsibility at an early age and, through it, tested and retested their fears of the outside world; others were slower and more cautious. Were I to attempt even a superficial ranking of my subjects in terms of their success—using fame, prestige, or productivity as a criterion—the most successful would show a definite rejection of fathers or mothers as omnipotent authorities, sometime during adolescence.

It is often thought that freedom goes along with assertive action. Yet, it is instructive to see how, for some of these men, personal freedom means the acceptance and indulgence of their needs for passivity and isolation, the denial of daily turmoil, and a turning away from what would seem on the surface to be obvious ways of achieving self-independence. Similarly, one would expect the research scientist to keep his eyes open and his senses alert. However, some of these men see their work as a way of helping them to keep their eyes closed to troublesome outside affairs, and as a way of denying the reality which has made them feel unhappy. Possibly scientists must keep their eyes closed to outside affairs in order to be good scientists; to label this shutting out of irrelevant externals as merely repression, denial, or isolation—as it might be labeled in other psychological contexts —would be to deny perhaps one of the most positive and liberating aspects of functioning as a scientist.

❦ Sensitivity

SOME HAVE CALLED uncommon sensitivity to experiences—usually sensory experiences—the first great phase in the evolution of the creative experience that leads to original work. This sensitivity may involve heightened awareness to all kinds of stimuli, in terms either of sensory processes or of some persistent or recurrent relationship between them. The curiosity about these experiences and the desire to seize them and put on them a personal stamp, or to delve into their more complex ordering, leads to the desire to create and the effort to produce a creative product.

The psychological tests showed that sensitivity in scientists finds expression in these ways: in their thinking, they are responsive to sensory experience data; they seek out

105

subtle and delicate impressions; they show a strong capacity for sensuous gratifications; in relationships, sensitivity is evident in their awareness of themselves and their own motivations; and in their discernment of the feelings and moods, wishes, and desires of others—without necessarily being responsive to them. They also have a desire to integrate internal and external experiences in a comprehensive way. Such a listing may give the misleading impression that the scientists' sensitivity extends into the many areas of personal functioning, that it is not necessarily confined to certain classes or objects or to certain kinds of experiences. This is to some extent inherent in the definition of sensitivity as increased perception of the world within and without. In the case of these intellectual men, however, their constriction, discipline, and unusual involvement in work make this the area in which their sensitivity is most readily stimulated and in which it is most generously expressed.

I expected the experimental findings to corroborate notions of the scientist's heightened sensory acuity and his keen responsiveness to order or disorder in external phenomena. Here my expectations were confirmed, but I had not anticipated that their sensitivity would be as readily directed toward themselves and to their own motivations. Overtly, these men do not show a great deal of insight into their own motivations and needs, although a few have become sophisticated in the field of psychology through reading. Yet there is a good fit of personality with scientific vocation, which means that, at least unconsciously, the scientist has been aware of his needs, and of the kinds of experiences and situations and areas in which he might function successfully—and he has acted upon these insights.

There is one aspect of the way sensitivity finds expression to which I would like to draw specific attention, and that is how this sensitivity encourages in these scientists what Kierkegaard has called the "paranoid leaps." Heightened sensitivity is accompanied in thinking by overalertness to relatively unimportant or tangential aspects of problems. It makes them look for and postulate significance in things which customarily would not be singled out. It encourages highly individualized and even autistic ways of thinking.

Were this thinking not in the framework of scientific work, it would be considered paranoid. In scientific work, creative thinking demands seeing things not seen previously, or in ways not previously imagined; and this necessitates jumping off from "normal" positions, and taking risks by departing from reality. The difference between the thinking of the paranoid patient and the scientist comes in the latter's ability and willingness to test out his fantasies or grandiose conceptualizations through the systems of checks and balances science has established—and to give up these schemes that are shown not to be valid on the basis of these scientific checks. It is specifically because science provides such a framework of rules and regulations to control and set bounds to paranoid thinking that a scientist can feel comfortable about taking the paranoid leaps. Without this structuring, the threat of such unrealistic, illogical, and even bizarre thinking to over-all thought and personality organization in general would be too great to permit the scientist the freedom of such fantasying. And as we shall see in the chapter on thinking, their own cognitive patterns provide internal boundaries and limits which parallel those of the scientific method itself.

One might say that scientific thinking in a way institutionalizes paranoid thinking; it sanctions it not only as proper, but also as the irrational that ultimately promotes the rationality of science. The manipulative nature of scientific models is a case in point: it is common knowledge that occasionally the same phenomenon can be explained by two different models, and that there is no right explanation which necessarily excludes the other. This equivalence of models puts a premium on the cleverness of the scientist, on his ability to concoct fanciful enough or diverse enough explanations to encompass phenomena—and there is a chance that any number of explanations will aptly fit the same empirical data. This encourages free rein to imagination and to the breeding of "crazy" ideas. As one zoologist has said, "One can maintain some crazy ideas for a very long time in science before enough evidence is accumulated to prove you are wrong."

Scientists say that ideas are very cheap, but that ideas that ultimately stand the rigorous test of reliability and validity are not nearly so abundant. The scientist with a vested interest in an idea sometimes holds to it with great tenacity; it may seem that he wishes to make it impervious to the rules and regulations which particularize scientific thinking. In the end, however, these ideas do not become part of the great body of learning unless they can stand up to the rigorousness of scientific scrutiny.

❦ Narcissism

OLIVER LAFARGE has said that scientific life is shaped by the feeling that the ends must be good not for oneself, but for all mankind; and that the scientist must be able to set aside personal advantage, comfort, and glory in his developing effort to make progress. Were this true, all scientists would have to be extremely masochistic, self-denying, martyr-like individuals. Few of our subjects would clinically fall into this category, and yet there is no question that they are dedicated scientific men.

What one sees in their personality pictures is neither selflessness nor selfishness; in their overinvolvement in work, in their fantasies about their omnipotence, in their anticipated accomplishments, in their minimality of interest in others who cannot further their own ends or goals, they are self-oriented. Yet their gratifications come as much from their contribution to the fund of knowledge and from what they contribute socially as from personal gains; in fact, their personal gains seem in some ways neglected.[6]

In relation to creative endeavor, narcissism essentially implies a need to produce and to value one's own products as an extension of one's self. Psychoanalysts have found that while excessive narcissism is a characteristic of the infantile and neurotically developed person, a total absence of narcissism is impossible for psychological sustenance in the mature adult.

One cannot, unfortunately, measure quantitatively how much narcissism is optimal for the individual. As yet, psychology provides no appropriate measuring sticks. Nor do we know exactly what to measure, or how to measure its role in given behavioral settings. P. Federn has presented some qualitative considerations which suggest that narcissism is "healthy" if narcissistic fantasies are slanted toward realistic tasks, relationships, desires, and activities that have a specified goal, and when, in the process of reaching this, a great deal of intellectual work is accomplished.[7] Goals are to be examined continually and critically so that they change and are adapted to realistic conditions. The classification of whether narcissism is "healthy" or "ill," then, depends not on the fact of finding the narcissism but on the use to which it is put in the personality and the way it is integrated with other aspects of personality functioning.

These scientists are fascinated with their work, and it is significant that some can hardly tell anything about themselves without telling in great detail about what they are doing currently. I have learned from these men about *Drosophila*, for example, about visual pigment in the eyes of certain animals, about brain pathways. Their narcissistic involvement is also evidenced by what one chemist has expressed in this manner:

Well, to me, science is terribly exciting. I'm not saying that the satisfaction comes from just having solved a problem; the satisfaction really comes—as far as I'm concerned—in the achievement of an understanding. I feel I'm understanding how the earth was formed, for example, or approaching an understanding of that. That to me is exciting—just solving one problem in connection with that is not terribly exciting, except insofar as it tells me a little more about what the ultimate answer might be.

Now in writing, where does the excitement come? First, it comes when you've worked over something, and you've written it. As a concrete example: when I wrote my first book, I was pleased with what I had written—that was the first excitement. Then copies of it had been sent to a number of people, soliciting comment, and the comments started to roll back. Have you seen the book? Well, look at these comments, for example. [Shows me a book jacket.] Well, you've got to be an iron man if you don't become excited. If one were able to do science without machinery, the excitement would be equal; but in writing, where there is no red tape, no organization to worry about, no budgets, you just go ahead and write. It's different from science where, unless you're a theoretical physicist and just need pencils, you have to go out and get money, and you've got to keep the people who give you money happy. You've got to write reports and hire and fire people. All of these are things which I personally find distasteful, yet the actual workings of science and achieving of results is wonderful, comparable to the joys of writing—very equal. But you have to do more work to get one than the other.

How narcissistic is such involvement with work? This question cannot be answered on purely psychological grounds. Since evaluation of narcissism rests on direction of endeavor, means used, and goals set, these have to be taken into account also. Whether a goal is appropriate for an individual or not, for example, depends partly upon the values that the goal

110

embodies and partly on whether the practices in meeting the goals are acceptable in terms of the larger societal ethic. Such considerations, if not completely decisive, are certainly not irrelevant. Thus, despite the fact that narcissism is a concept derived from intra-individual psychological functioning, and should be able to stand exclusively on a psychological base, we must use sociological referents to supplement their definition.

This inclusion of outside values, goals, or reference to complete psychological categories seems paradoxical, and yet it is not peculiar to the problem of narcissism. It is implicit in many other value judgments that are made in the psychological context, and a recognition of this fact has been one of psychiatry's significant contributions. In recent years, psychiatry has recognized and appreciated that a value system is inevitably built into a judgment about personality and personal functioning. Value judgments are seen as inevitable: first, because of the relativistic framework that defines functioning, and second, because criteria for adjustment would not otherwise have the necessary flexibility to encompass differences among individuals. In deference to scientific method, however, psychiatry does insist that the value system used in any evaluation of personal adjustment be made as explicit as possible, so that the system itself may be open to study and critical investigation.

I press this because I think it will help indicate what devotion of one's psychological energies to scientific work means in terms of psychological adjustment. When Freud attempted to define maturity, or—in his vocabulary—"geniality" or adjustment, he postulated that none of the mature person's efforts or energies was devoted to inhibiting or holding back of impulses; rather, that all were directed or channelized into creative, productive expression. This he held to be true of sexual as well as of aggressive energies. In an elaboration of Freud's position, Kris later pointed out that

111

these sexual and aggressive drives, instead of being expressed directly, become neutralized in order to allow for intellectual or artistic work. Freud used the term "sublimation" for defense mechanisms that were used in mature behavior. The working for social good, or toward the achievement of social aims, was always part of the definition of sublimation and it was specifically different from "reaction formation," a defense mechanism which also often resulted in a great deal of "social good." In this latter case, however, the "social good" resulted from the individual's attempt to deny and conceal other impulses that were not ego-acceptable.

In practical application, the differences between reaction formation and sublimation are difficult to draw; in fact some psychoanalysts, such as Frederick J. Hacker, say it is almost impossible. When the establishment of a difference is attempted—as is attempted in every intensive psychological study—the value system of the psychiatrist is inevitably drawn into determining what is really in the service of society, free from inhibition, and what is not. Even with one's own value system as a reference point, this is very hard to judge.

The empirical study of the psychological make-up of research scientists seems to me to reinforce the position of those who maintain that adjustment is inevitably a socio-psychological question, rather than a purely psychological one. Our reference points to looking at the ways and manners in which human beings apply psychological capacities and characteristics inevitably introduce sociological or cultural considerations; without these, there is no way of defining what is in the interest of society or mankind. For scientists, this means that the very fact of doing socially valuable work gives them a leg up on the ladder of adjustment. There is no question that their work is considered to be of greater significance, and certainly of more social import at this time, than is the work, say, of accountants or bookkeepers, or any job which may also be socially oriented but does not have the same prestige.

In summary, then, the empirical study of this group of scientists shows that in emotional and motivational characteristics, they are more different than alike. Their personality pictures cut across diagnostic classifications and classical personality configurations. As a group, they would be labeled as character types, with many men's adjustment falling within the normal range and others described as personality trait disturbances or character disorders. Furthermore, the stereotyped depictions of the scientist as a person given to mood swings, or depressions, or on the other side, overly controlled and logical in his emotional makeup, have not been borne out. On the contrary, in all these aspects there is a wide range of reaction pattern, much more so than one might have expected in the light of the long-standing and deep-seated impressions that have existed in the public mind.

The areas in which common denominators among the group are found center around a few main areas: the deep-seated investment in intellectual things; the expression of a wide gamut of emotional response within the intellectual (and particularly work) framework; the independence in emotional behavior—a feature which mimics the independence that will be noted in the analysis of cognitive patterns in the next chapter; sensitivity both to himself, to the motivations of others, and to sensory and even sensual stimuli.

The tremendous role of self in work is first noted in these data (a finding that will also be confirmed in subsequent material); for science becomes the area in which the strong curiosity drive is directed, the center of conflict, the hub for much of emotional experience—especially the intense experience. While, in this setting, work would and does normally engender anxieties and tensions, the data show too that anxieties are kept fairly well in check, because they

113

are intellectualized, and have become ingrained in the personality structure. This, plus the lack of other neurotic features in the psychological pictures, suggest that the researcher in general shows a characterological picture. When the adjustment of the man is somewhat disordered it does not necessarily bring much psychological discomfort. In fact, if it takes a toll in behavior, it is in the direction of making him function less effectively than he might in the light of his potential; or even making him "too adjusted," and thus not allowing his spontaneity to come through.

The study of the personality makeup of the scientists has shown us too that the resources, abilities, and personality characteristics of an individual can and do serve him in a number of ways simultaneously. The very constriction that enables a scientist to focus with little disturbance from outside emotional pressures, to work with dedication, absorption, and devotion in intricately detailed and often very demanding scientific problems, may severely incapacitate him as a husband or a father. The emotional constriction may also make him so socially inept that he seems habitually unresponsive to the needs of others. Still, diverse personality characteristics may not be as conflicting in the total personality picture as they at first appear. While some courses of conduct demand certain personality features and resources, others involve quite different abilities; and frequently psychological energies and characteristics are inevitably contaminated with each other. This makes them difficult to sort out, but perhaps it is this entanglement that enables the men of science to lead their complex lives.

NOTES

1. No specific intelligence tests were administered to the group because no test has sufficient spread in the top ranges for se

superior a group. Therefore, these classifications were approximated from the form-level ratings on the Rorschach Test.

2. The Dutch scholar, Johan Huizinga, takes issue in *Homo Ludens*, London: Routledge & Kegan Paul, Ltd., 1949, with the oft-repeated notion that science is merely a game. He has shown that scientific work cannot be subsumed under the definition of play, which occurs within certain limits of space, time, and meaning according to fixed rules. The rules of science, by contrast, are not unchallenged for all time, but are constantly being reformulated. Science also has outside contacts with reality, has purposefulness in its relation to that reality, and is sustained by more than mere pleasure. However, within the closed precincts of its method there are certain parallels: the scientists' continued penchant for system tends in the direction of play, as do the capriciousness and manipulation within the system, and the competition. Play, like science, is far from random, and reaches a very high degree of order in certain circumstances.

3. Max Weber has put this idea poetically: ". . . whoever lacks the capacity to put on blinders, so to speak, and to come up to the idea that the fate of his soul depends upon whether or not he makes a correct conjecture at this passage of this manuscript, may as well stay away from science. He will never have what one may call the 'personal experience' of science. Without this strange intoxication, ridiculed by every outsider; without this passion, this 'thousands of years must pass before you enter into life, and thousands more wait in silence'—according to whether or not you succeed in making this conjecture; without this you have *no* calling for science and should do something else. For nothing is worthy of man as man unless he can pursue it with passionate devotion." His whole essay, "Science as Vocation" (in H. H. Gerth and C. W. Mills, *From Max Weber*, New York: Oxford University Press, 1958) is a fascinating presentation of "the inward calling for science."

4. For two interesting biographies of the man who has been called America's only truly great scientist, see Muriel Rukeyser, *Willard Gibbs*, New York: Doubleday and Company, 1947, and L. P. Wheeler, *Josiah Willard Gibbs: The History of a Great Mind*, New Haven, Connecticut: Yale University Press, 1952, Rev. ed.

5. G. Klein and his team have conducted some interesting studies distinguishing individuals according to their various perceptual or cognitive styles or "ways" in which their minds work. They find there are individuals who are "levelers," e.g., those who tend to ignore differentiations, when confronted with certain perceptual stimuli, as

compared to "sharpeners," those who make differentiations. Their studies on "focusing," which relate to how easily people can integrate or dissociate themselves from the distracting or intersensory effects of competitive stimuli, hint that there is more here than simple cognitive processes related to making or avoiding distinctions, or success in cutting out distractions. These "styles" seem to be related to highly generalized, deeply ingrained attributes which are closely related to modes of defense.

6. In *Science and the Social Order,* London: George Allen and Unwin, 1953, Bernard Barber has pointed out that the morality of the scientist differs from the general morality of a liberal society in two ways: (1) the value of commonality, whereby everyone can share past knowledge for everyone is expected to contribute potentially to the future; (2) the value of disinterestedness or other-orientation, to use Parsons' word. Although the scientist's notion of success is directed toward him personally, success is sought by enjoining him to serve himself by serving others. This is partly true in liberal society where people are expected to make some contribution to the general good.

7. In P. Federn, *Ego Psychology and the Psychoses,* New York: Basic Books, 1952. See especially Chapter 16, "On the Distinction between Healthy and Pathological Narcissism," pp. 323–364.

I V

The Scientific Styles of Thinking

IN THIS STUDY I CHOSE TO MAKE no judgments about the scientists' creative abilities, since there seemed to me no measures of creative talents that could differentiate among members of a group whose general capacities were so high. Previous studies in this field had shown that the problem of evaluation in a field like creativity which is difficult to define to begin with, and elusive to study, is an extremely troublesome one. It is fairly easy to pick out a completely noncreative person from one who is talented, or even a somewhat original thinker from a highly creative one. Here some measures—such as amount of productivity as defined by number of publications, or scientific

117

rank or recognition as indicated by membership in honorary groups, or ratings of colleagues—have fairly successfully separated creatives from noncreatives. However, when a group of scientists of distinguished talents are compared with each other, such measures are not sufficiently refined to be useful or valid.

All the men in this study had gone into a vocational field which puts a premium on originality, imagination, and new ideas. It seemed to me in setting up this criterion for inclusion in the group that people without any creative abilities would scarcely have gone into research, knowing it would be difficult to fulfill requirements for performance, and to compete satisfactorily; and certainly they would have had little opportunity to move up academically, since promotion is usually based on performance in research. The demands for achievement are so tied up with mobility in academic circles that a kind and level of productivity has been established that insures that most of the more talented people go into academic rather than nonacademic research. Therefore, while this investigation cannot actually claim to be a study of creative persons whose qualitative attributes have been rated or evaluated, it can be said to be a study of men who, by virtue of being in scientific research in an academic setting, tend to be part of the top levels in the scientific field. In fact, two of the subjects have won the Nobel Prize.

Traditionally psychology has treated the creativity issue in two ways: First as a higher level cognitive process; and here imagination, thinking, reasoning ability, memory, problem solving and other such aptitudes have been isolated and analyzed to see how well they reflect creativity and can serve as an index of it, or how well they compared with other criteria which were thought to be measures of creativity—

uch as ratings of performance by a superior, or evaluation by colleagues.[1] It has not been easy to pick out aptitudes which are reliable indicators of creativity and unmistakably tied up with originality or unique performance, because performance seems to be so intimately associated with the second view of creativity—as a motivational process. In this view, creativity is seen as a function of sociological, or socio-psychological conditions, with the problem defined as that of bringing out talents in a gifted person. Under what psychological and personal conditions does a man perform in an original way, and what internal and external situations inhibit this talent?

Both of these viewpoints have highlighted a number of basic theoretical questions that as yet are unanswered: Does creativity exist in everyone, so that people can be rated on a continuum of perhaps 1 to 100, or very little to very much; or is creativity a unique quality found only in some persons? In the latter case, no amount or kind of sociopsychological conditions could stimulate it to fruition; in the former, these conditions become of crucial importance. But prior to this issue is the problem of identifying what aptitudes go to make up creativity. Certain psychologists in previous years have considered creativity as a general ability underlying all mental functioning; others see particular talents—for example, art or music—as each representing a kind of creative ability or set of abilities.[2] A further question is: What can we say about something that has been judged as a creative product in terms of the kind of talents it implies, and the future performance it predicts?[3] And it is possible that one can be creative although there is no evidence in a concrete product that can be looked at, judged and re-evaluated, and exposed to the discerning scrutiny of time?

The real difficulty that psychologists have had in coming to grips with these many problems inherent in studying

119

creativity is evident from the figures that J. P. Guilford
pointed out in 1950, when he found that of 120,000 titles in
the Psychological Abstracts, only 186 were related to creativity
imagination, originality, and thinking. He added, inciden
tally, that few of these have advanced our thinking very
much. In subsequent years another 300 scientific and artistic
investigations were done, which suggests that psychologists
have risen to protest C. Spearman's charge that the problems
in creativity have traditionally been solved by denying that
any problems exist—even though the efforts of psychologists
have in very recent years been somewhat beclouded by the
general tendency in our culture to call everything that is
new or novel, creative. This is a tendency Jacques Barzun
has recently called attention to when he described our "cult
of creativity"; and which as he suggests stems from the desire
to retreat from making judgments about how creative some
thing is, merely because the standards for excellence or
originality are ambiguous and ill defined.

This study was not directed at identifying the specific
creative aptitudes or particular intellectual abilities of the
researchers. It was aimed instead toward investigating the
ways these men thought about problems and perceived them,
the ways they would attack problems, try to solve them. The
projective tests, being unstructured and novel, demanded
that they take an ambiguous and meaningless set of stimuli on
to which they had to project some structure or meaning. This
was the way they fulfilled the instructions of the test, or
solved the problems presented to them. Then, looking at
their responses to the test stimuli, the judges could see what
general principles they employed to organize the ambiguous
materials. Their responses to the ink blots and to the vague
pictures of the T.A.T. represented their unique and idiosyncratic solutions to a loosely structured task.

In analyzing these responses, the judges looked at the

120

kinds of solution the subjects had offered—the content and context of the solution, and how they arrived at it: whether they used all the material or segmented it into little parts, for example, or whether they generalized from a few details, or interlocked many details before reaching a conclusion, whether the approach to every new situation that tests presented was the same or whether they devised different solutions, one after another, in trial-and-error fashion, to see which served the purpose best. Of interest also was whether the content they projected reflected their scientific bent or was so diverse that it gave little hint of their vocation—for were the latter the case it would suggest that they would relegate interests to the scientific situation, and not apply or lean upon these skills or interests outside.

Some of the cognitive hypotheses tested were related to traits like flexibility which applied to the manner of approach. The focus also was on the orientation or "set" in the man's thinking, the ways he looked at phenomena. All the hypotheses that were tested were derived from the literature about the way creative persons think and the ways they express themselves. Thus we were tapping both characteristics in thinking and problem-solving behavior themselves, as well as the motivational elements that get attached to thinking and intellectual aptitudes very early in life. I should mention that none of the notions specifically set out to describe the processes involved in the scientific method; I assumed that the logical procedures underlying the method would fall more specifically in the category of intellectual aptitudes related to reasoning which the projective tests would tap peripherally.

In addition, I analyzed interview data to study the way the scientists described their creative processes. Most of the knowledge that we in psychology have about creative processes are anecdotal, and rest on retrospective recall. Some of the most colorful descriptions of how famous scientists and artists describe their creative periods and activities has been brought together by B. Ghiselin. From these, as well as from the few attempts at experimentally analyzing how people create while they are creating, it has become apparent that the literary fluency of the men themselves as well as their psychological sophistication determine the insights they have into their creative processes, and their facility in communicating these to others. I have gone into the creative processes in this chapter to show the highly individualistic characteristics these take on among men who are in the single field of research, where patterns of operation are quite well institutionalized by the nature of the field itself. However, I think their descriptions serve also to indicate the kind and degree of psychological mindedness that exists among men whose preoccupations are primarily not with behavior, but in the natural sciences.

The results of the statistical analyses of psychological test data show that the scientists are a very homogeneous group in thought and perception. They organize and systematize material very similarly, deploying their intellectual resources in such a way that we can say they think about phenomena and look at them with a common orientation or "set"—not so far as content, but so far as the kinds of stimuli they look for and in which they become interested.

These are the ways of thinking and perceiving that can be said to describe the researcher:

1) He seeks to depart radically in his expressions and thinking from the usual, obvious, or hackneyed.
2) He displays novelty in ideational activity.
3) He shows an unusual emphasis in his thinking in the elaboration of fantasy.

4) He shows a richness in his symbolic and descriptive expressions and associations.

5) He has the capacity for recombining and reorganizing familiar conceptions.

6) He accepts reality but sees it in a way different from others.

7) His intellectual development is broad and he displays a diversity of interests.

8) His interests point to the theoretical and abstract rather than to the practical and realistic.

9) He prefers complex ideas and situations rather than simple ones.

10) He seeks out delicate and subtle impressions and is usually responsive to sensory experience data.

11) He can tolerate ambiguities and perception.

12) He can loosen or relax controls in thinking without showing personality disorganization.[4]

This means that there are certain kinds of stimuli to which scientists become alerted and certain stimuli they ignore. There are situations and experiences toward which they direct their attention; and they have developed characteristic ways to express themselves. These occur regularly, so that in addition to being "mental structures" that discriminate, select, and sort out what are likely to be important stimuli and what are not, they get to the point where they in fact operate as feed-back mechanisms, searching out from the mass of stimuli coming in those which are most likely to be significant. Thus these organizing or structuring principles take on an anticipatory or exploratory quality, as Gardner Murphy has put it, so that the perceptual field is scanned before the individual responds. Lawrence Frank putting it somewhat differently says that once some stimuli are perceived, certain others are automatically sought out and the bulk of others rejected. Thus, the ways of thinking become more than characteristic for what an individual does with stimuli he perceives; they become as well his "snail's feelers" in the world.

Applying this in the research situation means that the scientist goes into his work with a certain kind of scientific eye. Contrary to the stereotyped conception that the man of science is very malleable, open to every new stimuli, having a completely open mind, he is selective, discriminative, and quickly recognizes what might or might not be appropriate.[5]

Furthermore the thinking styles suggest the strong base in reality that the scientists' thinking has. It starts from something known, familiar, and well based in fact and only with this kind of solid reference point are new ideas or alternatives considered. Also, the final test of something original lies in the reality situation again. One physicist pointed this out and commented about the test stimuli, "This is completely unlike anything we do; we never start thinking about something that has no structure to begin with." (Needless to say, this is why I used the projective tests as the problem-solving task; it offers no cues upon which scientists can capitalize, but instead forces them to show what cues they use customarily in their thinking.)

The styles of thinking that this study elicited among scientists seem to have two purposes: first, keeping the men from being buffeted by the obvious and conventional stimuli, and directing their attentions instead to the new, the different, the out of the ordinary; second, becoming part of the mental framework, a regularly used set of mechanisms which because of its consistency and stability is conducive to creative thought. We know that certain psychological conditions encourage creativity and others thwart it, and we know too that thinking in bizarre ways produces anxiety. The really creative ideas have been likened by Kierkegaard to "paranoid leaps"—for they are antithetical to everything we know, everything realistic, every way in which we are accustomed to thinking about something. Because such "crazy" thinking takes one out of the reality sphere, one has to be a fairly well stabilized and integrated person, not to be threatened by thinking in bizarre ways, when controls are at a minimum, and letting one's unconscious take over. One can only think crazily enough to produce something really revolutionary or original when he has some strongly entrenched thinking styles on which he can rely and to which he can come home. Without these, the dangers to personality organization are very great, and so frightening that it would be unlikely that one could let his mind go to the fantastic proportions and distortions that are necessary to come up with a unique idea. Stylistic ways of thinking and customary ways of being oriented, become the intellectual stabilizers, part of the internal security, very much in the same way that reality does.

We learn further that the thinking styles, in becoming part of the way cognitive processes are patterned, are often rigidly set. One would speculate that in some men, they become integrated as part of their compulsive defense mechanisms, which are utilized for self-discipline, hard thinking, and long periods of persistent work. From the discussions of their creative processes we learn that such characteristics seem an inevitable and necessary, but unfortunately not sufficient, part of the creative process. While many anecdotes of great creatives have suggested the emergence of "inspiration" on busses (for Poincaré) or in bathtubs (for Archimedes) and have perpetuated the notion that creative thinking often occurs away from the work table, even such dramatic "break-throughs" are shown upon closer scrutiny to occur only after periods when concentration has been intense, where intellectual work has been purposeful, rational, and logical. There has usually been dogged persistence, tedious effort, and a clinging to long-sighted goals.

125

How these styles of thinking are related to creativity is an important question, because any search for an individual or group style or for a formula that defines creativity seems to defy the essentially nonstyle nature of creativity. Although we know that certain sociological and physical conditions can set the stage for creativity more than can others, we also know that there are certain ways of thinking that may suggest creativity and innovation and others that discourage it.

To turn now to the creative processes themselves, the interviews suggest that none of the scientists leaves discovery completely to chance. They have developed ways of working on and thinking about problems which they feel are more fruitful. I have recorded the following remarks on the process of discovery:

> If you never chase sidelines, you never find anything new; if you chase all the sidelines, you never find anything because you are running down too many blind alleys. . . . Delbrück's Principle of Limited Sloppiness: you should be sloppy enough so that the unexpected happens, but not so sloppy that you cannot figure out what happened after it has happened. . . . The better intuition a person has, the more you find out he is full of facts. . . . Lucky accidents don't happen to dead cows.

What these "words of wisdom" seem to add up to is that the scientist cultivates a state of readiness or a set for the unexpected. One physicist, for example, said:

> If I'm going to work on a problem, I never work in a way in which I have no ideas other than those that somebody else is likely to try. I don't know if you understand that, but take a problem such as the one I have been working on. The only ideas that I will pursue are those I choose specifically because it is unlikely that anyone else would have ap-

proached them in the same way. The reason is, if I do it in a standard way, it's a waste of time. Certainly there are many fellows who do it in standard ways and are very clever. If the standard way was the way out, certainly these other fellows would have found it, or will, depending on how much is involved. I am not going to waste my time on a standard way. The other guy can do that. I'm always trying to do things in a way that's different or original. If I have no different or original way of doing a problem, then I won't even bother with it. I'll go to some other problem. I'll always try to find a way to do a problem that nobody else has thought of—so far as I can tell. The result is that, when I finally do something once in a while, everybody on the outside sees it as a very original way.

Another chemist describes one of the "greats" in his field as never being satisfied with the conventional solution to a problem. He is always looking for an unconventional answer, and accepts the obvious only if something unconventional has not turned up.

Still another man describes how he has "trained himself" to have new ideas:

People have good ideas by having lots of ideas. But the way to have them is to start thinking. I make discoveries, have new ideas, by training myself to have them or by getting myself in the proper condition. Often I will work for a day, or two, or three, on some problem and not see what the solution is. Then I will drop it, but I think about it at night for a while before going to sleep. Then one month, or a few months later, I may suddenly have an idea that represents the solution to the problem. I think what has happened is that I've gotten into the habit of examining everything that comes into my mind with respect to this problem, and rejecting everything, until something comes along that looks as though it would be interesting, and then that is brought into my consciousness and represents "the flash of genius,"

127

as they say. So I believe this may be the way—or at least one way—to have ideas.

Scientists have many methods of wooing the unconscious. They recognize that the story of science is the story neither of the completely predictable nor of the absolutely controllable. As one theoretical physicist expresses it:

> You have to understand what we do. We take a flying guess at something and then we check whether it is like the experiment. This determines whether the theoretical idea or viewpoint is correct or not correct. But the question is on what viewpoint to try the experiment—that's the creative aspect of inventing a new idea. This thing is completely unscientific—there is nothing scientific about it. I don't know how it works. One guy gets an idea. Another guy gets an idea. Wherever they come from, they get ideas; but the question is how to check the idea. That you can do scientifically. You can make calculations on the consequence of the idea and see whether the consequences agree with what is observed. But the source of the ideas—that is completely irrational in a certain sense. It is not logical. And so when it comes to what ideas are going to occur to what kind of people—well, anything goes. I know nothing about the subject. All I know is that there will be a tremendous number of possibilities and varieties of ways that people will present their ideas when they first get them, and they are as different as night and day.
>
> I don't know how to compare physics to art or anything. I'm not going to make any comparison; I know only my own field. But whether or not there is a general knack or the same process for creating in every field, I don't know. Let me give you some examples of the reasoning in physics. Maxwell, who discovered the existence of radio waves before they were observed, predicted all the stuff. He had all the experimental results gathered around and tried to put them together and to represent them mathematically. He

put all the laws that were known in mathematical form, and when he had the equations together, he found they were inconsistent. But he noticed that if he added certain terms to one of the equations, they would fit together very beautifully, and as a result, he could predict certain consequences: the existence of radio waves. Now this particular method was the method of taking all the experimental results and putting them together and trying to express them mathematically. Everyone does that all the time automatically today; it's second-nature to us. Or take Einstein in understanding relativity. He had to have a different kind of philosophy about it. Everything by that time was formulated mathematically, but the problem was to try to understand these equations from a different philosophical point of view. Thereafter, people invariably tried that idea. In the case of the discovery of quantum physics, it was found that certain ideas in classical physics, that were there before, had no meaning. What one had to do in their case was to analyze very carefully the words: what they meant, what you needed to define them. So immediately, of course, this became the way for solving all problems.

Discovery has been made by a different specific method of attack. Today, everybody in physics automatically uses all of the regular techniques that we know about. Let's imitate Einstein, or this one or that. But every once in a while, there arises a difficulty that hasn't as yet been solved; it just keeps building up. The pressure from the unknown gets larger and more obvious. People have tried using the other methods; they're not getting anywhere. Then, someone is going to come out with a brand new idea, and it will have been almost completely unpredictable until after the fact.

To the scientist the irrational is interpreted in a number of ways. It can refer to the intuition which, as one scientist says, is quite divorced from understanding; it can pertain to what has been called the scientific *Gefühl* by scientists who try to surround the looseness of "feeling" with some reference in the direction of objectivity; it can refer to the preconscious or the unconscious fragments of ideas that precede communicable ideas; or it can be described as luck, the lucky guess, or serendipity, once the notion proves successful. Scientists cannot reject the irrational because scientific folklore is too full of examples of discovery that point to the influence of the nonrational, and their own experiences bear this out. They find that in their own scientific work they cannot stick purely and completely to the secondary process of controlled and critical thinking. They are forced to be aware, however dimly, of how all the thinking processes are related to each other on a continuum, how unsteady is any tight differentiation between the various levels of experience, and how the various types of thinking merge readily into one another and become demarcated again.

These researchers accept the irrational without any feeling that this involves a narcissistic blow to their reality-oriented egos. Instead, the scientific process becomes defined, in part, by the seemingly unconscious, unrelated, and off-base notions that precede scientific ideas. Consequently, they put considerable effort into actively participating in the process of liberating their imaginations, of training themselves to be receptive to ideas, of consciously discarding the old and searching for new tangents, of manipulating images and scientific notions, of paying too much or too little attention to hunches. How much recognition a particular scientist gives to the irrational, and how manipulable he thinks it is, seems to be as much a function of his psychological comfort with himself and his drives as anything else. It depends also on the personal security he derives from the scientific method. The method, with its system of checks and balances, serves as a built-in regulator which controls the "crazy" ideas or half-baked notions. The way science works—with its rapid network of communications, and the checks provided by the method itself—provides the reinforcement of reality principles, and this permits scientists to let their imaginations go with much less anxiety and doubt than they might have otherwise. It is as if they knew they would inevitably be brought up sharply by the external ego of science if their own egos were to distort and refashion reality a little here and there.

Some scientists feel themselves at the mercy of their periods of creativity. One chemist said:

> When I am quite creative and fairly excited I have a hard time sleeping and my memory is poor. Now again perspective goes along with the other periods. Of course, the really fine person is a person who can turn it on and off. He can have perspective one day, when he is picking his problem from the general field, and the next day, when he wants to be creative, he can forget it. The thing he is doing today is the most important thing in the world, and that gives him tremendous incentive. But I can't turn it on and off. I wish I could. The best thing I can do is make use of these periods for whatever they are worth. I don't know what they are made of. Maybe an embolic A or something. Maybe a kind of stimulation. Maybe your sex life, or heavens knows what. The best you can do is make use of it when it comes. When it comes, use it for all it is worth. My recognition of these things has come with time and thought and with analysis of myself.

Here is how a theoretical physicist describes his creative periods:

> You're working on something. Now when you are working very hard, the ideas are coming good, and you're beginning to solve something. I don't know what happens—you're not daydreaming, but you have moments of absolute blankness because everything is going on inside. Suppose you have had a mild success and temporarily you're stuck a little, thinking of a new direction in which to go. Then maybe

you start to daydream: first you get a great glee and pleasure out of the thought that the problem is breaking open. I don't know where this comes from or what it is from. You just like the feeling of seeing how it works, of being able to solve it. Maybe it's the same thing that makes people climb Mt. Everest. Maybe it's curiosity—I don't know what it is. You just get a big bang out of something that's working right. Then you get the human element in it. You walk around and imagine the paper you're going to write on this problem that has been existing all this time. The paper will be only about six lines long. And everybody is going to look at it and say, "It's so simple!" Of course, it's never quite that way, but this kind of crazy daydreaming shows how involved and interested you are in the problem and in the fact that you're going to publish the results, and people are going to read it. There is no question in my mind that this is an important feature because it's an inevitable part of the excitement and it gives you the drive to pursue the problem.

In the light of the sensitivity with which these men describe their own creative processes, it is surprising to see how few psychological insights are applied in judging creative potential in students. Here instead researchers look to concrete evidence of productiveness, or to some peripherally related characteristics. One zoologist says:

The only measure I think I find a little bit useful in selecting who is a creative student and who isn't, is to talk to the person about different kinds of subjects and see what questions he asks—how unorthodox they are and how broadly they range.

It seems to me creativity just consists of the ability to take facts and put them together in all sorts of new ways and bring out novel combinations of them. I think that most of our experience in our life tends to make us uncreative. That is, we take facts and concepts and put them together in ways that the people in the past have told us about and in ways that are socially approved.

One astrophysicist, who describes himself as a "poorly organized man, one who is far from systematic, and who depends mainly on intuitional flashes rather than on really hard work," gets his ideas not so much from sitting down at the work bench as from talking with people and thinking about things as he talks. In the young student, he thinks, creativity is accompanied by an appearance of youthfulness. He says:

I would say that most people who I feel are creative in science keep acting very young even if they are not. It's a strange boyishness among people I have encountered. The very good, successful, famous scientists throughout the country look and act years younger than they are—and some of them are actually silly and childish—but this business of youth is an odd thing. When I see some of my students coming in, and they already look to be forty years old, I get the feeling that they've had it already. This characteristic of youthfulness, I think, is second only to the characteristic of rapidity of understanding and skimming the top of a subject matter, in contrast to plodding through, getting a lot of data and then producing data from established principles.

A number of scientists have tried to single out characteristics which, they feel, are so intimately associated with creative thinking that they may in fact be predictive of it. One physiologist considers invaluable the ability to recognize a problem as soluble. He says, "You have to learn to back out and not try to do something that's insoluble. That's something I suppose you have to learn." Another scientist also separates the very creative men from those who are just competent by this characteristic. He says:

The creative ones tackle problems that can be solved within one's lifetime or even faster. They can be theoretical or experimental, but the ability to choose problems, to organize one's time, are just about the most important qualities of creativity there are. I studied under a professor who for many years had to do a tremendous amount of classroom work, do outside preparation, marking papers and the like, and yet he was an extremely creative research man. Of course, he put in more time than the others, but also he was very efficient. He could turn out a routine job, and in five minutes become immersed in research. He was never the kind of man who would spend ten years working on a problem and then conclude he couldn't finish it. He always had his work pretty much mapped out in advance.

One man conceives of scientific work as bridging the gap between what he sees and what he imagines. He uses very tangible criteria in selecting students:

When I have students and attempt to evaluate how creative they are, I look for things that are not in themselves creative. I look, for example, for the ability to write, and I have found that a person who is a lousy writer could never be any good in his work. For some reason, the qualities go uniformly together. I also look for neatness in work habits, for ability to take responsibility, for the idea of asking questions and not believing something or being too easily convinced.

One wonders whether such considerations as these really favor unorthodoxy and the unconventional or actually screen them out.

Scientists generally regard the borderline between the creative and the nonsensical as a very thin one; therefore they may—for reasons quite unrelated to the ones given here—put their weight on how well or how efficiently imagination is handled or, to paraphrase Lawrence Frank, on the "discipline" in the "disciplined imagination that is science." One biologist says:

When we look for creativity among people on the level we see on the staff here, it becomes obvious that creativity con-

134

sists in seeing the old facts and putting them together in an unusual way. You see this ability in various degrees among my colleagues all over the campus. Some people have this ability to make these new notions, to sort and to segregate very easily, but many of them get so involved in these ideas that they practically become screwball notions. It leaves scientists saying to other scientists, "Oh, he doesn't have both feet on the ground. Oh, he's got all these screwball notions." Scientists have many ideas that do not prove to be good if you promote them in public. I know one poor fellow who has the following disability: he has a tremendous amount of creativity and the ability to have all sorts of ideas on every conceivable subject, but he has very poor ability to discriminate between them subsequently. He has a tremendous emotional investment in any idea that he gets, so he defends the bad ones and the good ones with equal vigor. He's always in a peck of trouble.

A plant physiologist considers critical analysis to be an important feature in the creative person. He says:

The ability to criticize your own results is important. When you're young there is a kind of allowance for being carried away with an idea, but when one leaves the role of student, one has to develop a sense of self-criticism. We have witnessed a number of people in science who have been unable to see their own results in a critical light, and this can be very sad.

I compared the perceptual and cognitive processes of the experimentalists with those of the theoreticians. I had assumed that, in the test results, theoreticians would show strong integrative tendencies and preferences for synthesizing, abstracting, and generalizing as compared to the experimentalists, who would be the detailers, the men who would look for differences and for distinctive characteristics among the test stimuli.[6]

Neither this nor the opposite was true.[7] In fact, t͏
striking thing is that the test records indicate that both
these characteristics are regularly combined in both typ͏
of scientists.

The scientists themselves are divided as to whether t͏
distinction between theoreticians and experimentalists
merely one of convenient classification, or whether the diff͏
ences reflect cognitive variances built upon physiological
personality characteristics. To support the former positio͏
some men point to their own careers in which they ha͏
moved from one type of investigation to the other. F͏
example, one man said:

> Scientific work is something which individuals pursue in
> small groups of people—two, three, or four—without any
> relationship to anything. It's an unworldly sort of activity.
> It can be quite naïve and unsophisticated, and within this
> field I think my interests have shifted. They have shifted
> from a real preoccupation and interest in analyzing things
> (no matter how small or irrelevant) to a greater interest and
> enthusiasm for making syntheses of this analytical detail,
> and to relating items or collections of knowledge in one
> field with those of another. This tends toward working more
> with the ideational than the tangible aspects. This gets one
> away, in a sense, from the day-to-day pursuits of things in
> the laboratory. I used to know these tendencies in older in-
> dividuals when I was young, but I could never understand
> them. I always thought that this was sort of an earmark of
> senility. This was a peculiar way in which old men's minds
> worked. I always thought this was to be condemned and
> that nothing but what young people were doing—I mean
> getting to the laboratory twelve hours a day, pursuing the
> work, getting the data out, collecting facts, explaining the
> questions—that this was understanding and this was the goal.
> I definitely have found this to be supplanted. It makes some-
> thing of a conflict because now the young people around me

are wondering, I am sure, exactly why I don't do as they are doing.

Another describes the intimacy of the interplay between theoretical work and experimentation, suggesting that the increasing scope of the scientific fields themselves has given rise to this separateness:

Well, creativity and originality are good if they lead to something. If a man has bright ideas and does nothing about them, he is not making much of a contribution to society unless he is able to get somebody else interested in them. Now theoretical physicists do tend to determine the nature of experimental work. Sometimes the experimentalist has his own ideas, but experiments in physics often are suggested by the theoretical man. In chemistry this happens less often. We don't have a well-defined class of theoretical chemists. Most chemists are a combination of experimental and theoretical ones. That is, most good chemists combine the two actively. In recent years, however, because chemical theory has become so complex and difficult, we have found many theoretical chemists who just do no experimental work.

In their discussions of science, the men indicated clearly that they consider the theoreticians the aristocrats of science; the experimentalists feel that the theoreticians are intellectually the brighter. The way one experimental biologist describes his work points to this:

I have always liked to sit and do motions—techniques that require repetitive motions, like dissecting cultures—for it gives you a chance to think about what you are doing. You can't help it, and you have an opportunity to observe when you're doing this. If you just sit and say, "This is the kind of experiment that would be good to do," and hire a technician, and tell the technician to go ahead and do it,

137

I don't think in my case it would work. First of all, I couldn't keep up my interest that way. Secondly, I wouldn't have any ideas because I think when I'm working and doing mechanical, routine work—and for this reason I like to do it. When I'm doing it, I'm looking and thinking and deciding: what could this mean and what could that mean. I think there's a lot to it. I think a lot of discoveries are made by people who aren't very bright, who are intelligent but not phenomenal, not brilliant, but who are willing to sit down and do lots of hard work and to think about it as they do it.

It's almost sure that in biology, the field of science in which I work, if you do almost anything intelligently and do enough of it, something will happen that will be interesting. If you're sensitized to it and spend enough time thinking about it, and you know what to do about it when you come upon something interesting, you'll be a productive scientist.

This is more difficult in other fields, I think. You can't do it in order to be a creative mathematician. You can't do routine mathematics and become a creative mathematician any more than you can play the piano in a routine way and become a creative pianist. I think that creativity at the level of experimental biology is a different thing from creativity in theoretical fields where you either are terrific or you're no damned good. It's like music—you're no good in music unless you're terrific. It isn't true in biology. You can be mediocre and be an important contributor.

I think you should go from biology to chemistry to physics to mathematics where it gets more difficult. I am sure that no matter what my training had been or what factors encouraged or stimulated me, I am just inherently incapable of being a creative mathematician. I just don't think I've got what it takes. I think I could do mathematics, go through routine courses and learn to do routine things, and maybe do some little things that were significant, but I don't have the right combination of what it takes to be a creative mathematician or a theoretical physicist.

This man has made some of the most notable contributions in biology today.

An astrophysicist similarly alludes to the superior ability of the theoretician in the way he describes the work of the nontheoretician as "the dirty work":

This business of making extremely rough guesses, and building a chain of them, and coming out with a prediction that will work when detailed, is a characteristic of what I think is a good scientist. It certainly is the way I work at things. There are other scientists who just sit down and work out every decimal place in a chain of twenty arguments. Each one probably has a 50 per cent chance of being wrong. I think it's a very bad thing to work out details when everything you're doing is a guess, followed by another guess and another. You have built up a great chain of guesses, each one of them worked out exactly, but each one has a 50 per cent probability. You're wrong ninety-nine times out of a hundred—literally, if you have that many guesses. I tend to let other people work out these things. It's more exciting for me to get a first picture of how things might be; other kinds of people will do the dirty work.[8]

These stereotyped notions about a hierarchical structure within science based on abilities seem to be promulgated by scientists themselves. Many of this group describe the great scientists as "artists"—and by this they always mean the theoreticians—and the others as "guys who are painting." One, who prefers the vocabulary of football, says, "It doesn't make a damned bit of difference how many yards you make up and down the middle of the field or the number of first downs; the only things that pay off are the touchdowns, and the theoreticians are the men who make these."

139

Some men make a great effort to avoid placing any val
judgments on what are the most significant scientific cont
butions, and, though they talk about differences, there is
question that these differences have specific levels in th
implicit value hierarchy. One scientist said:

> I tend to think of scientists as belonging to two generally
> different categories: those who leap from pinnacle to
> pinnacle, or at least from point to point—without fre-
> quently being able to say what the detailed logical steps
> are between point A and point B—but somehow do this
> because it seems that it ought to be this way. These to
> me are the intuitive graspers. To this group belong the
> synthetic organizers of our scientific past—the Newtons,
> the Einsteins, and the physical scientists, the Darwins and
> the biological scientists—people who saw things sort of
> *in toto,* because it just seemed to them that it ought to be
> that way. You can take ideas and manipulate them into
> new configurations and put them into different kinds of
> boxes, etc. Intuitive scientists I think constitute the small-
> est number.
>
> Then I think there is the much larger number of non-
> intuitive scientists. The ranks grow daily because I think
> it makes up the majority of the people we train to fill the
> gaps. I am not intending to put good or bad value judg-
> ments on these. It doesn't have a value judgment. They are
> both good in the sense that they contribute importantly to
> what we consider progress. Neither can do the other's job.
> To be able to work out the detailed processes—that's very
> specific in itself. I think of these scientists (though it is not
> usually seen this way) as the "mathematical scientists," who
> work out each step in the equation and may come to re-
> markable conclusions such as the intuitive person never
> comes to. All in all, I think the techniques used are dif-
> ferent in these two cases.

Although the psychological test data cannot give a
conclusive evidence about the origin or development of t

cognitive and perceptual styles, one would speculate that they are stable, consistent, regular and ingrained parts of the characterological makeup of the individual. Psychology to date has not answered the question of whether intellectual capacities and abilities themselves are genetically determined or environmentally conditioned, and present scientific thinking suggests that the answer to this question will never be found in such a dichotomous conception of the problem.[9] However, regardless of origin, the fact that these stylistic characteristics appear in the personality test data as they do suggests that they are longstanding and at least operate as if they were an integral part of the psychological makeup of the individual, not readily manipulated or subject to change.[10] Some of the scientists themselves, however, have interesting ideas about how they learned to be oriented to the different and the original, and how they learned to conceptualize problems in certain ways. For their reflections we turn to some of the interview data. First, an anecdote from a physiologist:

My father had a toad which had been skinned and stuffed. It was a paperweight on his desk, and it was an interesting thing. A number of people were sitting in his office one day and were examining this thing. The foot, or the paw—whatever you call it—was missing, but generally you didn't notice it. I spoke up and said that I wondered what happened to his foot or something like that. Well, none of the others who had been looking at it noticed this, and everyone remarked about my picking up a detail of this kind.

One chemist says:

I can't remember what the years were, but I can remember working as a child through the Handbook of Chemistry and Physics, working through the tables of properties and substances, trying to discover irregularities that hadn't been

141

recognized before. At any rate, as far as I knew, they hadn't been recognized before. I was trying to carry on what we later call research, and I was trying to discover systematization of nature pretty independently, I think, of anybody else. This was something that had never been suggested to me but something I decided to do spontaneously.

The scientist whose father had trained him from very early days to be a scientist still conceptualizes physics problems in the ways he first learned to think about them. He says:

My father read things to me from a set of the *Encyclopaedia Britannica* that we had. We would read at first about dinosaurs, for example. I remember that he would sit back, and we would look at the pictures of these tremendous animals, and he would explain how long ago it was. In a sense, he would translate the things he would read. He would say, "In a hundred million years—do you know how much a hundred million years is?" Then we would both make some kind of an analogy for the total period of the earth. The total time for the earth might be, for example, a city block, and we would see how long it was. In the first part of the block, we would see that nothing much happened—not even any life. Then in order to indicate where the dinosaurs were, we would put them down on the very last two inches—or however it would come out, maybe the very last quarter of the inch strip. My father would say, "What does it mean for the dinosaur to be sitting here six feet across?" or something like that. He would say, "Do you know what that means? It means that he would come in this window. He would try to; he would come in, and he couldn't sit; he would break the sides; he would be able to put his head in the second story." He would stop and think what everything in the *Encyclopaedia Britannica* meant. I have exactly the same habits now. Every time I read something or try to figure something out, I try to understand the proportions in the same way. He taught me that, and I know exactly what it does for one, because I use this technique myself.

Not all scientists restrict formative experience to their earliest years. Some recall how ways of conceptualizing problems were taught them at the college level, and how these stand them in good stead today. One chemist describes his way of visualizing a chemical problem:

In science we teach everything the wrong way. We give all the descriptive material first. Then we get down to basic principles at last. That's the way it is in chemistry. When you become a junior, you begin to get down to the basic principles a little bit, and understand how chemistry works—that's physical chemistry. Physical chemistry is very difficult to learn, and it was very difficult for me. The professor, whom I regard so highly, taught this class in such a way that you could never solve a problem just by substituting numbers in a formula. In fact, he taught the class so that you couldn't work any problem—and we had lots of problems every day—unless you thoroughly understood what you were doing. It was well worked out, very smart. He told us every day, "You've really got to understand what you're doing." He would talk about every principle, and he tried to get everybody to visualize the principle, but we were talking about it in the abstract. If we were plotting something, we had to see what this represented physically. All of a sudden, I learned to visualize problems physically that otherwise would have been abstract, and to visualize physically the meanings of equations—things like that. I learned to be able to study things thoroughly without fooling myself into thinking I had understood something I really hadn't. I think I started this in Latin class in high school, and I finished it, or at least got it pretty well cemented together in this physical chemistry class.

A number of scientists however have instead suggeste a genetic origin for ways of conceptualizing problems.

> I think that no particular personalities of scientists go into one group or another. I have seen compulsive people in every scientific category. I think it is something more profound than such personality differences that determines any of these things. Let's take, for example, a common statement of biologists—"Oh, I want to go into biology because I am no good at math." Now I think that there is some reality to this—why they aren't very good at math or why they don't like the mathematical approach. I think it may be more profound than we think. I suspect it may have something to do with the basic structuring of the machine inside our heads, and that perhaps they can do things that the mathematically oriented cannot do, and vice versa. This may be the most basic kind of difference. I have no evidence for this—it's just a hunch I have, and I guess it was suggested particularly because you see the same personality characteristics in any of the groups. But you do see differences in actual abilities.

And from a chemist:

> I suspect that there are some people who do not run into details, who go to the heart of the problem. Other people never get to the heart of the problem because they are continually stumbling over details. Sometimes by doing this they make contributions. I think this must be pretty much in the inherent characteristics and temperament of an individual. I have never seen a person who started out thinking in one way, and then completely made the transition to the other by trying.

In summary, then, the findings suggest that researcher as a group have developed certain styles or characteristi ways of thinking and perceiving that tend to be the tools o organizing principles they use when confronted with un-familiar and unstructured data. While characteristically they do not work in scientific situations or at scientific problems in the same nonstructured way, it seems likely that the cog-nitive orientation they displayed in response to these am-biguous test materials also are applied to orient them to certain solutions and ways of looking at scientific problems. While the study did not tap the special aptitudes or intel-lectual abilities that are frequently identified with—al-though have not as yet been demonstrated conclusively in-dicative of—creative talents, it did suggest that certain motivational characteristics which "set" or direct thinking or the use of intellectual aptitudes orient the men toward the original and the untried. Additionally, the data reveal certain tendencies in manipulating percepts—recombining and reorganizing them, for example, which point up the efforts of these men toward making their endeavors orig-inal. As a group they tend to be discriminative and selec-tive, differentiating stimuli in very fine ways, thus making them their own, and also show the same tendencies in their descriptive processes. Their performance also suggests that they can stave off immediate and rapid closure, play with ideas through fantasy, tolerate ambiguity—and because these tendencies were also found in their developmental histories, we were led to speculate about how such stylistic character-istics develop, and how they become the ingrained parts of cognition that they obviously have become.

It was interesting to note that, in describing their own creative processes, these men who are trained in the ob-jective, rational and logical showed a high degree of respect for the irrational, the unconscious. They also had insight into the psychological conditions that seemed to stimulate and to inhibit performance in the scientific field, although when in the position of applying such insights to students whose creativity they had to predict, they retreated into

145

looking at attributes to which they could operationall
point.

1. The different schools of psychology have approache
creativity in very different ways. The Titchenerian introspectionists i
the nineteenth century explained all higher-order thinking processe
in terms of the unusual vividness, flexibility, and organization of menta
images. The Gestalt movement has brought out the active organizin
role of the individual in his perceptual processes, in contrast to trad
tional learning theory which has held that new responses emerge as th
result of mechanical and passive rearrangement of previously acquire
reactions. Some of today's cognitive theorists, using the language c
communication theory, see creativity as "having two aspects. The firs
has to do with the inventive activity involved in constructing highl
generic and widely appropriate coding systems, armed with which
person will subsequently, in a highly predictive way, be able to dea
with and go beyond much of the information he encounters in his en
vironment. The other aspect of the problem of creativity is the develop
ment of a readiness to utilize appropriately already acquired codin
systems." J. S. Bruner, "Going Beyond the Information Given," *Con
temporary Approaches to Cognition: A Symposium,* Cambridge, Mass
Harvard University Press, 1957.

2. I am using the words *talent, aptitude, creative abilitie*
interchangeably here, although they are not considered synonymous b
all psychologists. L. L. Thurstone, for example, in *Applications e
Psychology,* New York: Harper, 1952, states that it is possible for a ma
to have scientific talent, which implies the ability to handle competentl
the methods and concepts of science, without the ability to produce nev
ideas that are commensurate with mastery of his subject matter, whic
is creativity.

3. As Jean Piaget's work on the development of thinkin
and conceptualization in the child directs attention to sensorimoto
bases for intelligence, the question arises as to whether the units i
which we are looking at the cognitive abilities in the adult can b
framed so that they match the units of function in the young chil
This is a problem which plagues J. P. Guilford's and L. L. Thurstone
attempts to derive appropriate tests for isolating various intellectua
factors. My own hunch, which is influenced by S. Eiduson's thinking i

terms of the biochemical correlates of psychological functioning, is that early capacities become the mold on which the adult cast is made; that once the cast is made, the mold no longer exists in a recognizable form, and that the cast itself is changed through the fire and forces that have borne on it. Thus it may be extremely difficult to extrapolate back to what the original mold would be because the cast itself no longer fits the mold.

4. This is a reformulation of E. Kris's "regression in the service of the ego," which he has particularly applied to creative processes (see E. Kris, *Psychoanalytic Explorations in Art*, New York: International Universities Press, 1952).

5. This tendency toward structuring has been described by psychologists as "the focusing of attention." E. Schachtel has described the heightened awareness of a single stimulus circumscribing the play of our attentions in such a way that the flow of the more intuitive and unconscious processes is encouraged. M. Grotjahn has pointed this out in his analysis of the paintings of Hieronymus Bosch where certain focal elements are so unmistakable that they seem to have been intended by the artist to bring the attention of the observer to certain facets from which points, then, he might let his fantasies go. This seems to me partly the role that styles of thinking assume in the cognition of the scientists too.

6. My own expectations went along the lines of the typical sets a person brings to problems, which Kurt Goldstein has characterized along the dimensions of abstractness and concreteness. The person high in the latter would deal with what is given in terms of its specific identity, and would not tend to genericize what is learned; the individual who has very strong abstracting tendencies might not deal with the data that are given, except as an example of more generic classifications. J. P. Guilford acknowledges that this distinction foreshadows a main difference he has found in persons whose thinking proceeds more or less ably, dependent upon the content with which he is involved. A main difference rests between those who work more readily with figural factors perceived and recognizable (concrete) as compared with those who deal with conceived meanings and conceptual factors (abstract).

7. At this point I thought of what Thomas Henry Huxley once wrote: "The great tragedy of science is the slaying of a beautiful hypothesis by an ugly fact." ("Biogenesis and Abiogenesis," *Collected Essays*, VIII, New York: D. Appleton and Co., 1896–1902).

8. I would like to call attention here to the experimental

147

studies of J. S. Bruner et al., *The Study of Thinking,* New York: John Wiley & Sons, 1956, on concept or category formation which have outlined some of the processes involved in pragmatically *rational* or *effective* behavior. They have explored the ways in which the individual assimilates information, the strategies he employs to attain concepts, the ways he conserves the cognitive strain involved in the tasks, and how he regulates the risks of failure consequent to making and testing decisions. The introspective comments of our subjects offer excellent and lucid illustrations of some of the strategies and decision-making considerations with which Bruner's work has come up, for, as the quotations show, these scientists have given considerable thought to the behavioral sequences involved in their making judgments, to the cues they prefer to employ, and to the relevance of these to their overall objectives.

9. In psychoanalytic literature, increasing weight is being given to constitutional factors for style differences. H. Fries and P. Woolf have suggested that congenital activity types in the infant may determine his adult expressive style, and D. Rapaport has postulated that structural differences in sensory, memory, and motor apparatuses produce differential capacities to "receive" experiences from within and without, and thereafter put them to creative use. However, Guilford, who has extensively pioneered in mapping the structure of the intellect, suggests that it is obsolete to ask whether intelligence is acquired or inherited. This is too simple a question. Now this must be asked separately about every single intellectual factor that has been isolated. For a conception of the nature-nurture problem which is in line with modern experimental evidence in the biological sciences, see B. T. Eiduson, S. Eiduson, and E. Geller, "Biochemistry, Genetics, and the Nature-Nurture Problem," *American Journal of Psychiatry* (in press).

10. Cf. B. T. Eiduson, "Structural Analysis of Dreams: Clues to Perceptual Style," *Journal of Abnormal and Social Psychology, 58,* 335–339, 1959.

V

The Self-Images of Scientists

W<small>HEN A MAN CONSIDERS BECOMING</small>
a research scientist, he has some idea of the kind of work
and to a large extent of the kind of professional identity that
he is cutting out for himself. He has some notions about what
will be expected of him as a scientist, the rules and regulations that govern his work, the interrelationships of scientists,
and the values and ideals they share. These first conceptions
are often vague, romanticized, based on fantasy and myth;
they are modified as he becomes familiar with his work and
with the actual functioning and philosophic concepts of
science. It is not very difficult to communicate these to the
scientific novitiate; research science has had a long and rel-

atively stable history, and thus can present its roles an
philosophy in fairly institutionalized ways that point up th
coherences and continuities in the actions and reactions o
the scientific group. Once into science, one's own way o
thinking about himself in his work rests on these same
largely self-perpetuating concepts and images.

However, the most readily communicated aspects of be
ing a scientist are often those which do not govern the im
mediate end and the everyday circumstances. Ideals, in actua
function, frequently emerge as compromises. This often
gives rise to questions and doubts in the scientist about hi
identification with the group and about his performance
One well-established chemist, who is on the board of sci
entific journals, a consultant for government planning agen
cies, and a prodigious scientific worker with extensive pub
lications, said:

> One of the things I want to tell you is that I feel very
> anxious about whether or not I really act as a scientist
> should, rather than acting like myself. I thought of that
> particularly when I was taking this test. I was trying to ask
> myself, "What kind of things would a scientist see? Do I
> really see that, or do I see the things I think a scientist
> would see? Am I really putting on an act?" I am very
> aware of this, particularly when I give a lecture. I go out
> and give a lecture and think to myself, "I am acting like
> a scientist," but I always have in the back of my mind that
> maybe this isn't exactly the way I am. I think I am fre-
> quently bothered by the problem of whether in my work
> and activities I am able to do and think the way I would
> like to, or whether I am much more motivated to think
> and do the way scientists—or my conceptions of scientists
> —are likely to do. I think this is a kind of thing that
> scientists are frequently bothered with, because I know
> that some of the people with whom I have talked have the
> same feeling when they are lecturing, that it is not really

they who are lecturing but they as scientists who are lecturing.[1]

This suggests that a man's private image may not necessarily fit snugly with his public one, and that there is more to *feeling* like a scientist than simply doing the "right" things.

In this chapter I would like to explore what makes a scientist feel like a scientist, where his feelings of identity with other scientists come from, and the elements that seem crucial to making him feel like part of the group.[2] I shall do this by abstracting from the interview data the attitudes, values, and group orientations of researchers. These data were pulled out of answers to open-ended questions about what made the subjects go into science, what they had expected, how they conceived of science as a vocation, and why they thought others had chosen it for their work; also, whether there were any gaps between what they had anticipated and what they had encountered, once in science.

This group of scientists are men trained in the days of "old science," as compared with the new research atmosphere which Norbert Wiener has labeled, "the megabuck era."[3] In contrast to yesterday's intimate research environment where each man worked independently, decided what he wanted to do and the way he wanted to do it, and proceeded accordingly, using the help of others as he needed, but essentially conceiving of a complete segment of a problem himself, science has become a huge enterprise built on an elaborate hierarchical structure of many men using complex, expensive, rare technical devices and working with fantastic budgets. In describing this new scientific climate, Wiener has pointed to the development of the Ph.D.-research-scientist-turned-technician, the scientist who has become merely a cog in the wheel, the wheel which is so tremendous and intricate that neither he nor any of his "spokemates" know where the vehicle is driving, nor why, nor exactly where his skills or contributions fit. More important, he has no say about how the journey should proceed in the light of what he does. The most valuable scientific man is not the thoughtful intellectual of "old science," who was sensitive to the discontinuities as well as the continuities of the data, and adjusted his problem accordingly; but the superficial extremely competitive man who recognizes and accepts the fact that neither he nor any man can perform the new technical job alone.

In this chapter the backgrounds and traditional orientations of the subjects in this study should be kept in mind, for they represent one side of the changing picture; and many saw the above changes with misgivings and anxieties. Their doubts and questions about how these new attitudes would affect the traditional mores of science gave me the opportunity to see what changes would be taking place, and the direction in which they are going. I have included these data wherever possible.

One psychological by-product the nature of the change has made already evident: We have generally assumed in something so institutionalized as scientific work, the practices and philosophies of the field itself would be the determinants of the researcher's attitudes, values, and ideals. This does not seem to be the complete story. The present situation shows that it works the other way as well, and therefore, at the end of the chapter, I offer some speculations about how the practices of science may be influenced by the attitudes and personality makeup of the new researchers.

❧ The Scientist as Discoverer

ANALYSIS OF SELF-IMAGES shows that the scientists draw their main identity from their affiliation with the great discoverers, the great contributors to scientific

152

knowledge, the men who have given us the picture of the world we have today. Superficially modern scientists who are immersed in wind tunnels, scintillating counters, and chromatographic columns would seem to be far cries from the Newtons who watched apples drop from trees, or the Galvanis who looked at frog legs twitch. However, our data reveal that they share the same motivations as these great men and are primarily driven by the same curiosity about how things really are, and the same search for answers.

As one of the chemists puts it:

It sounds silly, but what I want is really an understanding of the pattern of the universe. Perhaps this is an urge for security—I mean knowing the pattern, but this is ultimately what I want. I would like to make a living at it, but I am quite sure that if I couldn't, I could make a living at something else. Sure I would like to be secure in my job but there are lots of secure jobs that I could have. However, I feel I would be kidding myself if I said that my interest in science is in anything but in the gain itself and the understanding it provides. All the status and the rest of it is kind of nonsense. Let's say I go out and win the Nobel Prize—so what? In fact, I would be very, very frightened to think I would win a Nobel Prize. If I'd won something like it, I would feel what I'm really aware of—not that I'm so wise but that the others are just fools. After all, Einstein didn't understand the universe either; what I would like to do is understand the universe for its own sake—but I am afraid that I never will.

Interestingly enough, this conception by the researcher of what he does and why, is the same notion about the scientist's motivations that has always existed in the mind of the public. Therefore, it would appear that the researchers are caught in the same stereotypes about themselves that exist in the general image, or perhaps to say it more properly, they have been drawn into science by some of the same fantasies that such stereotypes have stimulated.

This model of the scientist as discoverer might be elaborated in this way: he is a man whose "scientific impulse" drives him to discover new worlds and to follow up the implications of his findings; one whose personal involvement in intellectual problems and in abstract ideas and symbols makes him not only a discoverer, but even a creator of new worlds in which he then lives; one who is convinced that solutions to problems lie in the ideas provided by his own and related fields; one whose personal integrity makes him willing to state his biases and open them to scientific study. Thus, the ethos of science, to use Merton's phrase, which puts highest value on the pure search for truth, on objectivity, or the impersonal and the "uncommitted," are embedded in this main image.

Most frequently, the search for truth (in the men's self representations) is equated with discovery. However, it should be pointed out that the subjects actually separate originality from dedication and allegiance to truth in describing the qualities that are found in discoverers; and in fact, originality is ranked more highly, while truth-seeking is taken for granted.[4] V. Aubert has stated that the institution of science was born when the values of novelty, creativity, originality, and discovery had become sufficiently embedded in the culture to motivate large numbers of well-equipped people to dedicate their lives to the production of new ideas. The scientist became then not so much a man in search of truth, as a man who is permitted, forgiven, even encouraged and praised for making so many false statements—so long as he did not abandon his basic value for truth. Priority fights and scientific history also attest to the high rank that the values of novelty and discovery have taken on as science has become institutionalized.

Some of the interview data suggest this too. One geophysicist said:

> I think to me the greatest satisfaction is to be the first one to discover a new factor, to synthesize new data with an explanation. It is the feeling that you are the first to view this concept. When I say this can be the greatest reward, do not think I spend everyday looking for the various things; you know you have to do a lot of building blocks and a lot of paper work and a lot of punching numbers before you get that far, but when you do reach such a culmination and do come up with something new it is very satisfying. This is what I anticipated when I went into science—being on the frontier. I might have been influenced as a child by Hollywood, with its pictures of great scientists discovering things every minute, for there is no question that when I was a youngster the fact that I was going into work that would be on a frontier was very important to me.

Because of the strong self-gratifying element in these fantasies, a number of the subjects felt that they had to rationalize the way they subordinated the larger humanistic aims of science to their own personal satisfactions at work. As one chemist said:

> I think science is sort of an adventure since you never know what you are going to discover. I may be atypical as a scientist because I am not too interested in the knowledge of the field, or how what I do contributes to humanity. I am much more interested in enjoying the adventure of discovery. I don't get nearly so much pleasure as some people seem to out of finding out all of the details say, of certain metabolic problems, or of taking all the data into consideration—although I am sure it is necessary to comprehend these things in order to stay abreast of the field. But it's not the knowledge or its purpose that I find so appealing. I just like to be the discoverer of something new. For that reason I generally find myself working in fields that

155

are at the moment not too interesting to many investigators; in a way, I suppose my motivations aren't the same as others, but in a way, they must be, for the results do not reveal differences in the long run. None of us can ever tell when our discovery is going to be *the* discovery.

Because as this man has said, the great discovery seems within the reach of almost every one in science, for the results of experiments are generally unpredictable, we begin to get the answers as to why the discoverer image has been transmitted essentially without transformation from generation to generation: it is intimately tied up with the daily work of science, and reinforced by it. Science has been described metaphorically as patchwork or latticework or a huge unfinished puzzle, and in dozens of picturesque ways the "bit" as well as the "breakthrough" qualities have been captured. This means that every discovery is labeled a discovery independent of whether one attaches the adjective of "great and significant" or "small but worthwhile" to it. Every contribution regardless of size reassures the scientist that he has been a discoverer; thus the ideal "model" of the scientist is constantly extended and reinforced by the reality base that emerges to support it.

Furthermore, because the great advances do not seem—even after the fact—dependent on the individual qualities of the experimenter, or upon factors in the work that are necessarily dependent on the man's personal abilities, every scientist retains a notion that at any time he could be the great discoverer. A chemist's comments suggest how active and pervasive this attitude is in his own fantasies:

People who discover, who do the experiments, make the breakthroughs, have not done any experiments that are different from those I have seen. In fact, the things for which Nobel Prize winners get their prizes seem to be things I could have done in the laboratory. I read the stories of these men and they do rather simple, logical experiments—very nice experiments—but they are not terribly unusual, so that I think that if I happen to hit upon the right things, if it's in an important field—and I don't even think that is especially necessary—I know that I can become big and famous too. And any experiment, if it clicks, will be called, 'the great experiment.'

The fantasies around being the discoverer were rich, expansively elaborated, and show the great emotional investment that vitalizes the image. Another chemist describes how much he loves to be a participant in such activity:

I really have only two goals, I think; the first is the achievement of more understanding of the problems I'm involved with and have been interested in for a long time. The second goal I suppose is just to do what I can to help create a world where people can lead decent lives. I have no particular desire for a Nobel Prize or for vast quantities of money. I have enough money so that I can be reasonably flexible, and I really have turned down fairly good amounts and do all the time—because time—because time to me is more precious than money. One thing about science is that the search for understanding is far more exciting than I had ever expected it to be when I was young. It has opened up entirely new vistas of thought that I didn't think existed. The way it is played up at the present time, you would think it was all rockets and stuff like that. This is just an infinitesimal part of the whole. I love to be part of this great discovery and all of the exciting activity, and yet, when people ask me why I do other things such as writing and why I don't spend all of my time doing this, I just have to say that there are many ways that people can make contributions.

This man's comment suggests how this dominant image, like all elements which are pervasive in one's feeling of identity, becomes the yardstick against which one evaluates himself as a scientist. It defines the ideal type of man, the "pure scientist," as opposed to the non-ideal or impure. And the very positing of these "good qualities against the bad" shows how a moralistic or judgmental bias is built into the image. One man describes the pure scientist in this way:

> The pure scientist is one who is interested in a problem be-cause it is interesting and not because it is necessarily going to get him somewhere. If it does get him somewhere, fine; if it gets him an award, better. If he just solves it and finds out what he is interested in, it not only is worth doing but it also makes him a real scientist. I think this is what distinguishes the scientist from everyone else except maybe an artist. He has done something, he knows it's good; it doesn't matter how few other associates know it is good. It is worthwhile and thus it is really art.

Some of the men of this group, particularly the older ones who were originally engaged actively in research them-selves and find themselves now directing programs or other men, or diverted into historical and sociological aspects of science, have guilt about whether their present activities are as valuable as the original research they did earlier, and usually sense the feelings of impotence of which G. H. Hardy speaks when he describes mathematicians who have to write about mathematics because they no longer have the ability to contribute to new mathematics themselves. Such guilts and feelings of helplessness are often stirred up by the col-leagues who force them to rationalize what they are doing and they thus admit—as this man explained—

> I am afraid that I am not at the present time the ideal type of scientist anymore. You need all kinds; you can't have a scientific world that is made up of organization men or any particular brand of men. You have to have somebody

who creates new science. I am afraid, however, that by and large the people who create in science today are the young people who are continuously coming and going, the research fellows. They have learned enough so they can really do something for themselves. They have a few years before they can get saddled down with all the barnacles which older men get saddled down with and they have a few years in which they have lots of time to devote to making new science. The rest of us are not that kind of ideal scientist anymore.

This need for self-justification emphasizes how unmalleable the discoverer image is and how inviolable. It suggests indirectly too how serious and important the work of discovery is. Some of the scientists in this study simply say they have dedicated themselves to science because they have to know on what in their environment they can rely. And others acknowledge the personal needs to participate in the mythmaking for the world, thus supporting what Ortega Y. Gasset has said:

This is not so important for now as for the future, and in order to be tranquil now in regard to the minute that is coming, I need to be sure, for example that the earth which now sustains me is something which is here. The earth of the time to come is not here, is not a thing, and therefore I must invent, imagine, construct for myself in an intellectual schema, a belief about it.[6]

Because the self-representation of the discoverer is so basic to the scientist's identity, it essentially dictates how discovery should be done and more than that what the "right attitudes" are for doing such work. These "psychological conditions" are apparent in some of the self-images that follow. Those chosen for discussion here were the ones that occurred most frequently in the interview data.

159

❧ The Happiness of Pursuit

I FOUND in the interviews that every scientist spoke about how happy he is in his work. Each described work as fun, and as play, and said he was getting paid to do what he would have chosen as a hobby. Some tell of jumping out of bed in the morning, joyful in the knowledge that they will soon be doing the work they like the most. They rush to the laboratory and once there, coffee cup in hand, become busy immediately. However, they are soon involved with administrative duties, committee meetings, advisory sessions with students, budget maneuvering. During the entire day they are confronted with one problem: How can they squeeze a little research time into the mass of activities that have to be cleared away first. Some assign their research problems to their associates and to the technicians under their supervision, and then worry whether the anticipated results will be botched up by these less experienced workers. They fear—and apparently with some justification—that the "unexpected and often most important" parts of the research may be thrown out, and that the whole problem will fall to the "technician's level."

A few who insist on keeping their fingers "radioactive" —when no student is interested in the problem they have in mind, or when a problem cannot wait or demands their personal skills—engage in research by establishing an elaborate and ascetic work regime, a regime in which no phone calls are permitted, no personal communications, no interruptions. Frequently, research is even done behind locked doors. The work is difficult and produces anxieties. The men fret and storm, go home preoccupied and irritable. Once the problem breaks, they are faced with the new anxieties that come with the demand for writing it up and getting it into print before they are "scooped." Once this is done, reaction sets in. Often they hang around idly, feeling empty and vacant until they get started again. If the pressure during research is painful and seemingly interminable, the pressure between research projects is worse.

Their happiness obviously cannot be defined in terms of absence of tension or unabated pleasure. On the contrary, they are very tense about their work, and are frequently impatient and filled with despair; but their discomforts do not dim their over-all notion that what they are doing is enjoyable, and that no other work can compete with it in this respect. Mundane, "masochistic," routine work does not seem to destroy their enthusiasm. They, like the public who romanticizes science, never weigh the tedious hours of methodical and dull "scientific prying" against the occasional magnificent minutes of discovery. In fact, some speak of how much their pleasure is enhanced just by knowing that all knowledge is ephemeral, and that one never solves problems once and for all, but that the scientific game has an infinite number of solutions, and nobody really wins. Others speak of the work process as a series of ups and downs, where "the ups keep you up just a little while, for always they are followed by downs marked by a desire for another victory and a greater one."

This goes along with what we have learned in psychology: happiness and pleasure cannot be explained simply in terms of reducing tensions or of the constant and immediate satisfactions of needs. Evidently, a good deal of pleasure comes in the period when tensions are being built up, when rewards are delayed by circuitous and devious means. There seems to be something, too, in the mixture of pain and pleasure which seem to be contaminated in so many of our experiences.

I have transposed the expression "the happiness of pursuit" from the familiar "pursuit of happiness" to describe the pleasure scientists find in setting up stimulating situations, in meeting the challenges of the problems and the instruments, in slowly making progress on something that was very difficult. The outcome is not unimportant in their feelings of happiness and satisfaction, but it is not all-important. As one chemist has said, "Winning the awards is extra gravy." What apparently does make the difference, and even defines happiness, is finding channels that are thought to be worth pouring one's resources into—and then letting physical and mental energies go. The channels also have to be appropriate for one's abilities; otherwise, they are not sufficiently absorbing. Here is a chemist's view:

> I wouldn't be in scientific work if I didn't enjoy it, but I think my uncle's philosophy has always badgered me into this. His philosophy has been that a man should work to the utmost, whatever his capabilities. I don't really think I have any specific ambitions. I think the research I'm doing is worth while. I'm a little concerned about the fact that I'm being technically outmoded to a certain extent by chemistry, and essentially I'm an empirical rather than a conformative person. I've picked a tough problem in one of the few areas that haven't been done as yet, but I have the feeling that if I can't think of a good and difficult problem to do in order to use my abilities, I should do something else.

Thus, the scientist essentially takes "happiness" into his own hands. This may sound like a game of "positive thinking," but it is not. Scientists have been confronted a little too sharply with departmental demands, university restrictions, and conditions written into government contracts to be susceptible to such palliatives. But what they do say is that the core of happiness rests with the fulfillment of inner, rather than external, conditions. Because they are aware that happiness depends more on what one puts into science than what one gets out of it, they find excursive ways to get tastes of the great, but sometimes long deferred, pleasures. Some become quite exhilarated as they pick and choose between alternative problems, for example, or try to see whether they can refine old techniques by some unique adaptation that exhibits their personal skills to advantage.

The culmination of all this comes in their expansive feelings of freedom, and of the potentialities for choice. Some like the experience of knowing they can go for a haircut on university time, and that they do not have to report to anyone where they are going. Others enjoy knowing they are in a field which is so multistructured that it encourages any number of approaches, orientations, and practices. One organic chemist has put it this way:

This is an important motivation in regard to my becoming a scientist—this business of freedom. It is the feeling of freedom more than it is actually having it and using it. It's the concept of it or the feeling of it, and by freedom I mean broad choice. This is a profession, I think, which offers just about as broad a choice in coming and going, and doing what you please, as anything else I can conceive of. I could completely waste the rest of my life now, if I wanted to. I am free to do it. If I want to go to Europe, I can go to Europe; if I want to spend my days this way, writing books, I can write books; if I want to do research and write papers, I can do that; I can do whatever research I want to do; if I want to go skiing next week, I can arrange it—in fact, I am going skiing. In other words, you have tremendous choice, and if you want to be financially successful—if you're good enough—you can be. You can make a tremendous amount of money if you want to, or you can work on completely academic problems and not worry about patents and applications. Science is one of the few things, in my opinion, that is really moving in our culture, and not only is it moving, it is producing things which people can see; and so long as it is producing things that people can see in our kind of economy, it will be well supported. As a result, it is given freedom and a lot of it in big helpings. I wasn't smart enough to figure all this out to start with, but I always had the feeling that you had more choice and more freedom in science than you would in some of the other subjects that had their classic periods many years ago.

My concept of freedom is choice. It's made up of a lot of things—not only political or academic freedom but also choice in a lot of different areas—much of this stemming from my own resources, from my personal strength and my ability to use them. I have always had the feeling that the only thing that would ever limit me was myself.

Among some scientists the findings show that there is an inverse relationship between their subjective feelings of freedom and their objective obligations. They are extremely burdened with classes and with the huge administrative responsibilities that go with deanships and departmental chairmanships. Their time commitments are onerous, as is the seriousness of their responsibilities. But in almost every case they are vigorous men who have been carrying on this diversity of duties for many years, and who take pride in how effectively they move their attentions and talents from one area to another.

On the other hand, the heavy class schedules and the constant stream of students coming into their offices for consultation prevent some from being able to produce as they would like. The scientists who manage to avoid such distractions insist that the men who don't manage, "ask for it," that it is for them a "socially accepted escape from freedom," and a "decorous way of concealing that they are burned out."

As I listened to the scientists' opinions on happiness, I was impressed with two things. Most of the scientists carve out degrees of freedom for themselves with marvelous ingenuity and imaginativeness. They are few who believe that research can be stifled by even the most inhospitable external conditions. Although more favorable conditions undoubtedly could do much to promote more active scientific work, their need to make a wedge into or to counteract some of the limiting conditions seems to express the intellectual orientations with which they turn to the problems of science itself.[7]

Second, while few have stressed the compulsiveness with which many creative persons are bound to their work, their devotion to research, and their consumption by it attests to the attitudes that E. Erikson has described so dramatically in his *Martin Luther:* "A creative man has no choice. He may come across his task accidentally, but once the issue is joined, he has no choice. The task is intimately related to his personal conflicts, his superior selective perception, to his one-way will: he must court sickness, failure, insanity, to test the alternatives whether the established word will crush him, or whether he will establish a sector of this world's fundaments and make place for a new one."

❧ The Scientist as Genius

BEN SHAHN has said that people take great pride in having a Van Gogh painting on their living-room wall, but the prospect of having Van Gogh himself in the living-room would put a good many devoted art lovers to rout.[8] Analysis of interview data reveals that scientists share his compartmentalizing tendency. In science, the "geniuses" and the great men—unconventional as they may be—are honored and revered. But when the craziness or the eccentricity that sometimes accompanies the genius threatens to find embodiment in a colleague or student, there is a great rush to lock the laboratory door.

Every thinker who has revolutionized an area is regarded generally as a man who has been alienated from the values and beliefs of the society of which he has been a part, but today this getting out of his culture is acceptable only if it is so circumscribed that it is confined to the area of scientific thought, and does not spill over into the area of personal behavior. The "cult" of scientific "neutrality" has been interpreted as the "cult of scientific noninvolvement," and as such it has been put into the service of dissociating oneself from oddity.

Scientists do not have a simple time rationalizing this "split." It takes some internal juggling, which tends to go like this: "I have the feeling that very gifted people should be well balanced. I don't like the queer geniuses who are impossible. They grow up sometimes and accomplish great things, but I don't like to have them around. They're too difficult to work with, too hard to fit into the university." One man claims:

> These extraordinary people use me up emotionally; extraordinary people are difficult to handle when they are in numbers. The organization can tolerate just so much deviation, and I have to consider how one person's development will affect every one of my people. If I were dedicated to the idea of only making breakthroughs, I'd do much better to have just two or three highly selected people working for me, but I'm not. I like to break through, and then I like to have this exploited, so I get people who are plodders to work for me—just to clean up. Do you see my pattern?

The conflict is sharpened because scientists have a great reverence for the sagas of their eminent forefathers, sagas in which the need for the dramatic has perhaps emphasized the oddity and the curious in the great. They relate these legends readily and help pass them on. They seem to enjoy the identification with the eccentric who has become great, even though they cannot tolerate these capricious aspects in themselves and find the oddities in their coterie threatening. In a way, science is idol-oriented; the long-established custom of the authority vested in the great teacher has never vanished from the natural science tradition.[9] Almost everyone in this study followed his formal advanced university training by studying here or abroad with persons of great scientific reputation, and though some of the great men today do not have the power and status of scientists of old, nor have great centers of learning developed around them, their role as masters in the training of men coming up is essentially the same.[10] Such a relationship between authority figures and students promotes, under ideal conditions, an undisturbed alliance with tradition.

I should have said that scientists are idols-oriented because, despite affiliation with one teacher or another, there is little feeling that scientific work is done in one way, or that any particular great man is more representative of science and its traditions than another. The great men are not the great thinkers only. Apart from the few whose excellence is unquestioned—the Einsteins and the Plancks—there is dispute about who sits on the next rungs below them. Scientists have reservations about the men whose achievements have been built through the efforts of others. They have respect for individual talent, even when achievement has not been commensurate with promise, and they are fond of the men who have used their talents more to inspire others than to further private interests. The teacher is rewarded with a kind of idealization that is seldom accorded the scientist who is not a teacher. They are, as it were, the scientists' scientists —"the men Nobel Prize winners dedicate their books to," as one biologist put it when talking of a chemist who was the teacher of four Nobel Prize winners. Sometimes it is the scientist with infallible judgment in singling out promising students who is admired; sometimes the one with ingenuity in administration; sometimes the men with enviable creative vitality. And in each of these categories there are men who are called great. This diversity in idols has been possible be cause the men from whom the scientists trace their genealogy had only to meet minimum conditions of the classical sci entific model. That is to say, whoever the ancestor and wherever his laboratory, the idol operated in accordance with the same methodological principles that all scientists operate with, lived by the same mores, and in so doing fulfilled the minimal requirements. These were sufficient to make him a suitable and desirable predecessor for all who follow, and made for the tremendous variety among the idols to be idolized and the opening up of a storehouse of potential identification possibilities. Generally these idols are men viewed at a distance because once close at hand, the rose colored glasses through which they have been viewed too frequently get blurred. Yet some of this group, because of their own psychodynamic needs, discussed one great man after another in an idealized way. The great minds and the great imaginations continue to feed the fantasies and in fact even overextend them—and one gets the feeling that de spite the researcher's insistence upon rationality, knowing firsthand how rare great thought is, he has no alternative ex cept to lift his gods to Olympian slopes.

In this group, scientists recognized that what is begin ning to happen in the sciences is that the real individualist has a hard time surviving and coming through to the top.[1] One man contrasts the situation here with that in Europe; he feels that, although there are certain things abroad that tend to kill off individualism, there is still a greater opportunity to "be a screwball." The dangers that exist there arise from the lack of opportunity, and the necessity of keeping from trampling on important toes. "At places like Oxford and Cambridge," one man said, "the screwball still has a place Here the screwball has to struggle; I mean, he has to com promise quite a bit to make out. This is part and parcel of this business of mass production, because if you're producing large numbers of things, you can do so more efficiently by using people who are not very difficult."

In the United States, the students who are bright and well-rounded are often singled out as the promising talents in the profession. In one institution, which draws many brilliant and erratic youngsters and where there is a great deal of concern about how to motivate and bring their creative abilities to fruition, there is no question that a creative *and* adaptable youngster is more highly regarded than a creative but odd one.

The paradox between the idealization of the eccentric greats and the intolerance for eccentricity on the home ground is due largely, I think, to the changing nature of the practice of scientific work. The single or lone experimental investigator is rare today; though many scientists rebel against team research or interdisciplinary research, not too many actually do any investigation exclusively by themselves or with one assistant. The natural science fields have become big and complex; even the small and isolated segments are in themselves extremely intricate, entailing elaborate instrumentation, technical help, and approaches that a man can scarcely cover alone. Although students and technicians doing research are often assigned to one single problem and put under one man's direction, the project still assumes the nature of large-scale operations.

This undoubtedly has an effect on the selection of desirable workers for the group. The effectiveness of an individual depends as much on how he fits into the research group as on his own scientific abilities. Academic research settings are not structurally equipped to take care of problem cases. Their achievement drives depend to a large extent on the exploitation of those advantages that come from regular and consistent patterns of work. The large laboratory has to be a smoothly running operation in order to run at all, which means that it has to be an organization that is relatively free from conflict. Therefore, it puts a premium on a network of interpersonal relationships in which there is a minimality of involvement. Most of these men, therefore, feel that the scientist with unusual work habits, quirks, or emotional disturbance not only involves his associates in stressful and painful situations but also diverts the psychological energies of the group—energies that should be going into research. Those who demand more personal attention usually arouse such envy, hostility, and resentment in the others that the advisability of their continued participation in the program inevitably comes up.[12]

Because some of this same aggression that is so irritating in conduct can power the intellectual rebellion in creativity, scientists are aware of the dangers in this development. As one chemist says:

> It is very hard to decide at an early stage about who is the one who is going to originate an idea. Somebody who might be merely a "screwball" and not get any place afterward might be the person who could do it; yet these "screwballs" are not the persons who work well in groups—for example, in the lab I have here. The people who work for me have to be a little bit in the category of the bandwagon type; nevertheless you want to encourage them to do work on their own problems as well as on the idea. So far, I haven't had any really creative ones.

The crucial question is, of course, whether these changes in the way science is now practiced will affect the people who are drawn into it and impair their use of their creative talents. A number of scientists feel the way one man expressed it:

> Science is still a very personal field. You find that men who are uninhibited as individuals are uninhibited as scientists. Sometimes it adds to their ability a great deal to be this

way. Now I think you've got to be uninhibited in science. You won't make any progress if you are too tied to the past. If you conform too much there will never be any progress. From my own observations, I would say that you cannot divorce a personality or an emotional constitution from a scientific one.

Science, Chemical and Engineering News, and other journals that the scientists read are full of discussion about whether science still has a place for the individual investigator. The complexity of instrumentation and problems, the changing nature of scientific setups is repeatedly pointed out. However, they also point to the trend of some research organizations to support the individual researcher, instead of, or as well as, the projects that he does. They suggest that perhaps here lies the wedge for providing facilities and opportunities for men regardless of their personal idiosyncrasies. While even these career fellows seldom work any longer in isolated setups or independent from larger organizations, they do have the opportunity to pace the work as they see it, conduct it as they wish, and are in the position of being the one who sets up the conditions under which the work is to be done, instead of vice versa. So far too few of these career fellowships have been offered to permit systematic study of what their effects on research and on the researcher have been. However, one gets the impression that this trend is in the right direction, and were it continued on a larger scale there would be little opportunity, as one scientist put it, "for the tail to wag the dog."

❧ The Gentleman Scientist

INTERNAL COMPULSIVENESS has dictated the way scientists work at research. In this investigation almost every man spoke of his long hours, his seven-day week, and his complete absorption in his research problems. In fact, these kinds

of efforts have become so mechanically affiliated with scien
tific work, that they seem to have become merged with th
values of scholarship, rigor and discipline, and represent th
only "proper" ways they can be seriously pursued.

In research one finds the attitude that personal and pro
fessional satisfaction—and even to some lesser degree, re
sults—are proportional to the investment of time and energy
Empirical studies on the origins of American scientists hav
pointed to the strong components of these Protestant ethica
tenets in their backgrounds.[13] This achievement ethic ha
been supported in their own careers by the fact that thei
scientific performance is judged by colleagues—and the gen
eral public—by what they have done over a long period o
time. Seldom is a major award or prize given for a specifi
accomplishment. Scientists themselves are suspicious of
sudden and never repeated triumph, and the public has com
to associate real distinction with superior performance in
field over a span of years. Thus, persistence, patience, an
tolerance for monotony become virtues in morality pattern
There seems to be no place for the dilettante in science, th
man who as one subject put it, "sticks one toe into the wate
of research." Except for a few dissenters, the subjects showe
unanimous agreement in feeling that the aims of scienc
could not be met with lesser devotion, diverted motivation
or as Karl Deutsch expresses it, with a more "commercia
orientation."[14]

Now into the hallowed atmosphere dominated by suc
attitudes and ways of practice has come a maverick in th
form of the "gentleman scientist." For him this moralit
pattern does not appear appropriate. In fact, he has bee
called the "gentleman scientist"—not because he wears mor
fashionable laboratory garb—but because he has more ele
gant laboratory manners.[15] He keeps regular hours, usuall
maintains a 9–5 schedule, and after 5, turns to other interes
—literature, music, art—what one biologist called, "the goo

fe." He is interested in things other than science, and deberately takes time and energy away from scientific endeavors to devote himself to other pursuits. Thus far, the gentleman scientists are all young and eager men wanting to make a career for themselves in science, but not at the expense of other pleasures. There is no question that they breed anxiety in the puritanically oriented.

The anxiety that these men have about the newcomers is whether they will be moved by the same personal concerns in regard to work. Will they, for example, think about how adequately they are fulfilling the scientist's commitments—the question which plagued the chemist quoted at the beginning of this chapter? Will the gentleman scientist wonder whether his private role is an adequate expression of the role of the revolutionary thinker, the intellectual rebel, the scientific frontiersman? Will he have anxiety about what he does, not because these anxieties are the expression of neurotic inner doubts or of poorly established personal identification, as they might on the surface seem to be, but because he views these anxieties as the inevitable self-inquiry that plagues almost everyone who takes this work seriously? They emphasize that the gentleman scientist's intellectual dissatisfaction with ready and conventional solutions, his unrest with established ways of understanding reality, has emotional and personal implications. Thus, to them an important aspect of the scientist's self-image is an element of ambiguity in his own identity.

They wonder whether tomorrow's researcher will experience similar unrest; and if so, how he will juggle these "right" motivations—which provoke his interest in science in the first place—so that he is placated, appeased, and in some way integrated into the work situation of large-scale science, which apparently has little use for him.

Some of the older and established men are aware that their concern over the gentlemen scientists may be in part reaction of older people to the changes their successors in evitably introduce, or to the implied criticism of their own practices. There are other worries, however. One man said

> I have the feeling that the students we get have less of the sacred fire than the students of my day had. I think this is true even if you allow for the nostalgia in looking back. I think there has been a real change. You can say, "Well, we're getting older, and it appears this way to us," but I think there's a fair amount of softening up in society as a whole—and scientists have followed the same process. I think it true even now. There's a tendency in many places to have less rigor and less scholarliness in the work that's coming out.

Another man says:

> Scientists have got to be industrious; they've got to be motivated; they've got to feel that what they're doing is important. We have a lot of students who suffer from lack of challenge—but some of them, I think, demand too much to challenge them. We have lots of bright students who don't want to do anything well unless they can do something very important and very spectacular. Well, we're stuck in this—because it's terribly hard to think of something very important and very spectacular to do. There are a lot of other people who have already tried to do this, and a graduate student's chance of doing this is very slim. His just sitting down and in the abstract thinking "what's going to revolutionize biology? That's what I want to do," isn't going to get him any place, because he can't get started. This is actually a tremendous handicap. He may be extremely able, and he may be very brilliant, but nothing happens because he won't settle for anything but the spectacularly important—and he's usually smart enough to know what's important. Here his cleverness is a disadvantage, for he won't do anything unimportant.

Actually, if he would be doing something unimportant, he might think of something important, but he won't think of it if he doesn't do the other—so he's trapped.

Students want to start at the top, do the "crucial experiment." If they're intelligent enough, they may often talk themselves out of the experiment that would make a great discovery because, in terms of what you already know, you can often say, "This experiment can't lead to anything interesting; therefore I won't do it." Yet the less intelligent fellow, who doesn't know it won't lead to anything, will do it. The fact is that if you don't know enough *a priori* to know what the work will lead to, something unexpected may come up that will be the great discovery. I think all these factors enter into the changes we see in science today. Researchers need to have real enthusiasm and real pleasure in doing their work—even though they're not sure that what they are doing is going to revolutionize things.

Is it just coincidence that these university people are observing on the scientific scene the same kinds of shifts in motivation—and possibly even in character structure—that have been described on other fronts by sociological observers? The "gentlemen scientists" seem to show the same extensity of experience—often at the expense of intensity, the same leveling out of differentiated kinds of emotional involvements, the leisure-time orientation invading the work area which have become the mark of the "other-directed man" and the "waist-high culturists." No longer does it seem to be knowledge at any price, but knowledge at the convenience and comfort of the scientist.

Even in this day of space rockets, jets, and atomic submarines, one scientist finds that:

The current discouragement or depression that you see so often in young people is bothering more scientists today

175

and keeping them from being effective. Everything today is seen to be humdrum, ordinary stuff. A great deal of our work certainly is that. However, there is the tendency of workers to switch problems, to work on something that somebody else writes up and that seems to be very hot. I'm sure that people who switch problems try to do something they've never tried before and find themselves in the same morass as those men who originally worked on the problems, and who, themselves, left the problems in midstream.

The above quotations present only one side; a number of other scientists in the group predict that constructive changes may well take place. One biologist feels that this shift in attitude may mean more thought and less jumping into immediate activity for American scientists, and thus some approximation of the contemplative attitudes that one sees in English scientists may result. Another questions whether discipline and its related values are actually lost. He says:

The one thing you can't be without or else you won't be a scientist, is ego involvement in your scientific work. You know, I think there's a lot less ego involvement in work in the people we're getting now as graduate students, the young people who come out of the schools that it's so fashionable to give help to, nowadays. These kids, like the students I have, are all ones who appear to be doing research because it's fun—and by the way, they work a lot less at night. They don't work so hard. The question is, of course, how much discipline and hard work you need to have, and the kind of discipline you need. My own feeling is that the discipline that leads you into not stopping work on a problem until you finish it, and not saying you understand something until you really do, is good, but that it is not necessarily related to creativity. That's discipline all right, but why should that be essentially related to whether society, the system, or the teacher encourages or discourages orthodoxy in expression? For the time being, I'm going to believe they're unrelated; that you can encourage people to think of all kinds of notions that can possibly occur to them, encourage them in this, reward this, and at the same time bring in the discipline with which he's then able to talk about all these notions, and really get involved with them, and pick out the ones that are going to be good.

I wonder whether the change in image—perhaps socially-bound as it is—could have been effected had not the practices in science been ready to meet it halfway. One feels quickened tempo and excitement in many scientific fields today, particularly in theoretical physics, in neurophysiology, in genetics, where bright young men, who have hopped onto discoveries because they were not too well indoctrinated in the conventional approaches to problems, have pushed into the forefront. But whether the unglamorous spadework will get careful attention, or whether the "gentleman scientists" will prefer to bask comfortably in science's uncertainties, remains to be seen.

❦ Sciencemanship, or the Successful Scientist

ALBERT DEUTSCH, who for the last few years had been visiting scientists all over the country surveying the research being carried on in fields related to mental health, had the impression that "there are a lot of scientists bucking for the Nobel Prize."[16] While a large number of the men in this study would consider that such scientists are not *real* research scientists, others would say, "Of course! Science is not the pure golden thing we like to think it is."

The code of science, what is acceptable behavior and what is not, and what are appropriate symbols of recognition, is peculiarly ambiguous. Scientists are not undecided about what should be done, but they are undecided about what the right reasons are for doing what they do. Whether a reason is right or not has no direct connection with the content of what they do for the most part—the uncertainty about whether to work on the A-bomb project in peacetime may be, for some, an exception. They are concerned more with how much they should be motivated by the tangible rewards that they anticipate from their work, and if "extra-scientific considerations" serve as conscious motivations, how much they will conflict with the impersonality, the freedom from bias, and the objectivity to which they are dedicated.

The ethics of science, refracted as they are in the scientific method that eliminates the observer from the observation, have incorporated the notion that personal considerations are nonobjective and must therefore be eliminated. Theoretically, the approaches to scientific goals can be systematically planned and laid out, the criteria for success appropriately determined, and rewards justly distributed. What happens, however, when such rigor is attempted with even so well-delineated and institutionalized a household as the scientific one, is that factors not carefully and thoughtfully accounted for tend to slip in through the back door. It is not unlike the value system developed in obsessive-compulsive patients who develop notoriously well-defined and rigidly adhered to standards for behavior in some areas, yet with equanimity flout these same standards flagrantly on other fronts.

Let's take the concept of success as an example. Many scientists use the word "success" only *sotto voce*. The notion of success as something that may be pursued, not necessarily won by merit, does not sit very well with them. These men share some of the clichés: that a truly creative person is motivated by pure rather than impure considerations—purity meaning that the reward should be thought of only in terms of inner satisfactions derived from arriving at the solution—

and that a desire for recognition, exhibitionism, or self-aggrandizement, if it emerges at all in such a person, is only an extraneous concomitant of devotion or dedication. They postulate that they and their colleagues are motivated differently from persons who go into business, for example, and that, therefore, the prevalent notions of business success are inapplicable to science. One chemist said:

> Scientists are also motivated by curiosity, but I doubt that the businessman is. Real research scientists are interested in a problem because it is interesting and not necessarily because it is going to get them somewhere. If it does get them somewhere, fine; but if they just solve it and find out what they wanted to know, it was worth doing.

The analogy to artists and the creative arts is more acceptable to them. Implicit here is the retreat into idealism, the identification with the creative man who was moved by stirrings from within rather than from without, and the preferred propriety of the ascetic reward.

On the other side are the scientists who think that to deny that scientists are driven by the personal desires for reward and recognition is to cast doubt upon what *is* the creative in science. Some men in every field are driven by jealousy and fantasies of omnipotence and desires for retribution; the same motivations unmistakably play a role in some scientists. The ingenuity to exploit whatever motivations operate in men of science is seen as the problem of the scientific society. This group does not deny the objectivity and impersonality in scientific method; but, accepting the notion that ambition for success need not mean a contamination of the scientist, they use as an analogy quantum physics, where the observer cannot be treated independently of the phenomenon under study.

Members espousing this position state that there is no

179

inherent disagreement between how science is done and how business is done; that, in fact, creativity and originality in science are facilitated by, and to some extent impossible without, the adoption of those techniques that have been recognized as the cultural modes for success. Some argue that the homogenization of the practices of business and science is not only inevitable, but has already taken place:

> I think it is also important to recognize that there are many parallels between success in science and success in business, for example. The way things are organized these days, science is very expensive; and when I went to sea on an expedition, we needed two ships, and the ships cost $1000 a day plus the salaries of everybody who was there. So you see, there's a lot in being a creative scientist today that hinges on being able to frame a problem, or develop a deal in research, and going out and enlisting support for it. There are many men, who are capable men, who apparently don't like to do this or are unable to do this. This is unfortunate because nobody will do it for them, and if they happen to be in a field which requires this kind of support, they will be at a disadvantage. There is another side to this which is rather like being a good salesman. Many times you develop what you consider a new innovation or a new idea. It has to be sold to the scientific community as well. By selling it to them, I don't mean from the standpoint of getting glory for being the discoverer or anything like that, but interesting sufficient people to work on this, so that they will continue it and develop other facets. So I think it's a matter of the sequence of papers that you write on the subject or the ideas you've developed—how you do it, how you present these ideas at meetings—so that if you have an important idea, it will not be buried. Sure, if your idea is important, it eventually will be recognized, but it may be discovered fifty years hence, as with so many of these things. On the other hand, the field could have been pushed ahead very much, had it

been recognized at the time and had others subsequently contributed to its development. I think there is something to putting together all the techniques we know which are very hard to define exactly in terms of procedures, but altogether these become very important in when and how advances are made.

These two divergent positions show that, as science assumes the complexity and processes that in America we know best through the development of commerce and industrialization, some scientists think the time has come for the reaffirmation of scientific values through the withdrawal into scientific halls. It is there that the differences in values and practices which define science are magnified. Others think that these values can best be reaffirmed by reappraising them in the light of the natural evolution of science as an institution. Neither position, it seems to me, is a denial of the inevitability of change. It is rather a question of—to paraphrase Everett Hughes—how, and how much, science as an institution has to change in order to remain the same.

Whether scientists like to admit it or not, success in science can be promoted. There is no Madison Avenue set of rules and persuasions, but success seldom comes by chance. Most scientists in this group have subjected their intellectual abilities to a good deal of critical analysis. They seem to have staked out areas that are particularly fitted to their types of talent. They have evaluated their own capacities in the sharpening-up processes with others, and then, quite consciously, they have decided how to compensate for their lacks or how to make the most of what they have. All seem to have taken for granted that there are set limits to their intellectual endowment, and yet almost all feel that they are the masters of their scientific fate. They are hardheaded, realistic, and have few romantic ideas about success coming to those who sit and wait.

181

The extra effort, the competition, the stamina, which are devoted to making the most of ability, are regarded with admiration for they tie in with the highest scientific values. "Creativity and originality," said one man, "are good only if they lead to something; but if a man has bright ideas and does nothing about them, he's not making much of a contribution to science, unless he happens to have the quality of being able to get somebody else excited about them."

Scientists seem to recognize intuitively how hard it is for men to come to grips with themselves, and how much effectiveness is lost until this does take place. One established chemist evaluates himself in this way:

> I feel, having been in contact with great chemists and knowing my own abilities pretty well, that I'm not the kind of chemist who will make his mark through intellectual powers alone, because I realize that there are many others who have far greater intellectual powers than I. However, I do a great deal of work and have been very productive. I have excellent opportunities in which to use my abilities, and I make the most of them.

Another, whose drive and imagination were commented on independently by a number of colleagues, says of himself:

> So far as I.Q. tests and all that kind of thing are concerned, I've done quite well, but not unusually well. By that I mean that my wife can beat me out in everything but mathematical problems. It has always been quite apparent to me—and it is particularly true as I get higher and higher in my profession—that I have been dealing with people who are, in an exclusively intellectual sense, more intelligent than I. They have better memories, better analytical ability, and things like that. The thing that always made me able to compete advantageously was my organization and my drive and determination, on the one

hand, and a certain amount of wisdom, on the other hand, which probably comes from my background previous to my becoming interested in science.

There is a high premium on motivational characteristics that tend to enhance the use of resources. The ethical standards that apply to such things as competition are those of the business world scaled down to scientific size. One chemist who feels science has always been competitive to a large extent thinks it has taken a turn toward a more gentlemanly trend, though perhaps at the expense of the psychosomatic health of the scientists:

I think many of the people in science are also driven by a great deal of competitiveness, but I don't know if it has to be that way. Whether they would actually do the same caliber and kind of work if they were not pushed is very difficult to say. Certainly quite a few chemists are very competitive in research. Ulcers play a big role in this business.

There is a tremendous driving force to be the first one to get to a problem, and there are many competitive people around who steal ideas. Certainly many of them act like children. This is very much out in the open for many, and yet a lot more repress these things, and you get the angry stuff coming out only occasionally, or you have to read between the lines. The old German professors got this out right away, of course. They wrote nasty articles about each other, called each other names, but nowadays scientists feel they have to be objective about everything, so all this goes underground, and the feeling about it is certainly shoved away from the surface. The whole problem of stealing ideas—who got an idea and what not—is certainly very difficult to talk about because this is the climate for producing ideas, and ideas come very readily.

How much competition is acceptable, and where gentlemen's agreements stop and fist fights begin, is not well-

183

defined. Some practices are tabooed as immoral, but others have a fine line of distinction. A recent Hart cartoon in *The New Yorker* shows two scientists in a knock-down, drag-out fight, with an associate saying to the head of the department, who is looking on, "It seems they were following parallel lines of investigation that suddenly converged."

One scientist said:

> Competition, I think, is a strong influence upon human beings, but as far as scientists are concerned, perhaps they have a little less of this than others. Two scientists who are working on the same subject, even if one of them might solve the problem before the other and thus cut the other out of any recognition, tend to cooperate. Even if a person is working on the same subject as I am, I know he is not thinking exactly the same thoughts, and the two of us together will probably solve it better than one of us alone. I may rather underhandedly not give him all the information I have if I know this information will allow him to solve the problem before I do; but I have a few qualms about this. However, I certainly resent it if someone has done something I've spent a year on, and it suddenly appears in the literature and spoils my year's work. Naturally I resent it. I don't think I resent the person, and I don't think the competition is as fierce as it is in many other fields.

The successful scientist has become sophisticated in the sense of trying to set himself for discoveries, "playing for the lucky breaks," and not being averse to doing what he can to be ready for them. This is not promotion in the business sense; it is part of the scientific game, the rules and regulations being known and used by everyone so that all are equal under the laws of chance. This seems to be related to the general notion that ideas are "certainly cheap in this game," that the "mind is actually very weak," and that whatever help can be given to make scientists aware and sensitive to what is going on around them should not only be encouraged but also be incorporated as part of the game.

The scientist holds himself in a state of readiness. In every anecdote of the right man at the right place at the right time asking the right questions or noticing the right things, it is apparent that the clues have been present for a long time, and that the final result arises out of a combination of circumstances. One physicist has stated that circumstances, at most, determine the historical time of discovery; and a biologist feels that because the scientific population is increasing in the world so rapidly, the probability of people having the same idea independently at more or less the same time is greatly increased. "There is a great element of luck in the exact time in which one has an idea and whether this ultimately becomes known as 'your idea.' "[17]

Scientists customarily lump luck and accident together, in fact, the word "serendipity" is defined as a combination of the two, yet one chemist illustrates the difference as he sees it:

Luck plays a role in scientific discovery, all right. For example, Carl Anderson was not looking for the positron when he discovered it; but if either he or Professor Millikan had not had the bright idea that cloud chambers would be well worth careful examination, the discovery would not have been made; and if Carl had not been a keenly observant and thoughtful man who asked himself, "What is the meaning of the fact that this track has the wrong curvature, and is it possible that the particle is moving from the bottom of the chamber to the top? Yes, that was possible, but should I not make conditions such that I know where the pattern starts and take more photographs and try to check?" Well, this sort of thing isn't luck, so the discovery of the positron was not a matter of luck only.

185

Yet there are discoveries that you can call accidental—the discovery of penicillin by Fleming is a standard example. He was not investigating molds at all; he was investigating growths of bacteria, and his technique perhaps was not too good. A little mold got in—that was accident—but then for him to look and say, "Why is it that there's a little bare patch around each patch of mold where the bacteria don't grow?"—that wasn't luck.

This reflects the consensus in this group. Many hold to the notion of the "prepared mind" with specific need for hard work before and after. Yet, quite a few cite examples to show that the "prepared mind" is somewhat of a misnomer. Too much preparation defeats the openness to the unexpected that should be encouraged and much of the preparation seems more related to abilities that are innate rather than learned.

You can do an experiment, and if it's an elaborate experiment, you have to make a succession of twenty-four choices to come out right, and you have to do every one of these right. Well, if you make a mistake out of the twenty-four decisions, the experiment is no good. Some fellows have the ability to make them right every time so their experiments come out. Another fellow who works equally hard doesn't get anything because he makes a wrong judgment. This is something that goes beyond knowledge; it goes beyond experience too; it's something that some people have, and some people don't have—this kind of judgment—and it's not always an objective judgment. Sometimes it has a big subjective component. I mean, most scientists aren't really objective, any more than anything else is one hundred per cent objective. They do an experiment or plot a curve, and the point comes off the curve. Well, then they have to decide then and there if the point is really a significant deviation or if it is an experimental error. What you usually do is to try it over; and the next time, if it fits the curve, you throw the first one away. That's not being objective, it's being subjective. Now you have to have a feel for this sort of thing. Should you have thrown the point away or shouldn't you have? If you made a mistake, then you missed something by throwing the point away; if you're right, then you have the sense of "Well, this experiment is working right now, and the point is off for some nonsignificant reason, so I'll throw it away." If it's off for a significant reason, then you've got to stop and find out why. There is a feeling for this.

With all due respect to innate abilities, scientists are aware that nonscientific techniques can help to make the most of talent or discovery, and they consciously borrow a few of these techniques from advertising. The attributes that make for success anywhere are equally effective in science: personal charm, capacity for fluent relating to others, tact for oiling the machinery of interpersonal relationships, all operate in the achievement of scientific success. Some scientists lump all of these into "showmanship" and include here not only the ability to put one's work across but also the selection of a field in which to work that might have more possibility for spectacular performance than others. As one chemist says:

The same results will be presented in a journal differently by different people, and salesmanship actually becomes a factor, I feel. You could argue that in the long run the impact on science is the same whether the results are well presented or not. But as far as a man's personal success goes, he can be recognized sooner and promoted faster if, in addition to his innate abilities, he has a sense of salesmanship. Nowadays, I think it takes more to amount to something; I, for example, think more of different orders of magnitude of contribution than I did before. Maybe this is not so much a matter of the times as something that is inevitable as you shift from first trying to make your mark in a field, and then continue in it.

187

The role of salesmanship is also stressed in a backhanded way by a scientist who describes the man with whom he worked for a long time as "winning the Nobel Prize in spite of his personality."

Perhaps it is an inevitable development that once the notions of success in the business world to some extent invade the scientific, the same tools that promote success in one are sought after in the other. This raises the question, however, of whether the facile, the easily smoothed over, and the persuasion by personal manipulation, if such behavioral techniques become acceptable to the scientific community, will eventually prove destructive to the quality of scientific work.

Lasswell has used the term, "restriction through partial incorporation" to describe the inevitable limits set to the natural progress of a group when that group is accepted partially by what was previously its enemy. Since the attitudes and aims of business and scientists have for many years been antithetical, we wonder if this is not the appropriate point to raise the question about the implications for science of their recent alignment. On the one side, science has been very successful, been regarded very warmly; in fact science professors have even been brought from all over the country to give seminars for industry's top level executives. Furthermore, during these years, science has been able to attack and conquer huge and important problems. On the business side, the picture is of an equally fruitful relationship. However, as the mores and the practices of the two become more interwoven, one wonders whether the same amount of rebellion against the traditional, the breaking down of what had been fixed, the questioning of the taken-for-granted, the distrust of the obvious, will be permitted science. These were science's seductive graces, the qualities that made it so tantalizing to business in the first place. Will they continue to flourish in the new alignment, and if not, if they do become adapted to the world of business, will not science's great value for business be destroyed after all?

❧ The "Model" Scientist and the Trouble with Models

WHEN THE CHEMIST at the beginning of the chapter wondered if he were acting like a scientist, or really being a scientist, he was asking two questions: one, how well his own identity emerged with the identity of a scientist as he conceived of it, and secondly, what a scientist was *really* like. In his statement and in the self-representations of all of this group there is an implicit notion that there is a "real" scientist or a man who is doing the "real" scientific duty, the hard, back-breaking work of science, putting in the effort where in the long run it most pays off: at the laboratory bench. It is this man who is the real intellectual, whose work is tied up with the main goals of science, its raison d'être, its conditions. Other functions are of lesser value; therefore the scientists who perform them are weaker and are less "real scientists." The model, then, is the ego ideal figure, who represents the ultimate position, and in fact, defines what a scientist should do, how he should think, how he should act. By comparison, everything else—all other work, duties, affections—is inevitably of lesser worth. We have seen in the way the scientists in this group rebuke themselves as they become old, distracted, sit on committees or government advisory boards, or become administrators—and thus move away from the ideal.

From this picture it is obvious that the scientist is hard on himself. He has built up a judgmental, critical superego which has a built-in, clearly marked scalar system, along which attitudes and kinds of performance are measured. When he moves away and deviates from the pattern—spending time, perhaps, organizing and directing chemical societies, or educating high school science teachers—he becomes a

189

maverick, or a person who has tossed aside the flaming torch; as he does if he holds back from merging himself completely with the "ideal," or proceeds to work outside the model, and never tries to approach it. These alternatives are all thought to be less valuable than performing the "true" work of the scientist. The mythopoeic conceptions of the group are narrow, and confined to the few dominant images of the researcher, and their ramifications, that this study has brought out.

Furthermore, these data show that the subjects are clinging to this singly oriented "ego ideal" now more tightly than ever; their hold is intensified as they sense that it might be giving way, and that the clear, readily distinguished and unmistakable symbols of their vocation are now becoming more diffuse, "softer," more ambiguous. For some men the original models are taking on a sacred cast, so that the man who turns away from them is being thought of as having been easy prey to pleasures, as having been seduced by fame and fortune. Only those men who have turned to public roles or advisory capacities after they have done their stint of research work, and are being thus rewarded for their efforts, and being given the privilege of taking on "greater" obligations do not lose status. Our scientists tell their students who think of public roles for themselves that the way "up" is to become respected, and the only way to be respected is to do research first. The basic alliances and affiliations must be first affirmed.

However, when one examines this dominant image against information about how scientists really work or what they do, one notes a discrepancy between the two. I would like to cite three kinds of information that would suggest that what scientists actually do is a far cry from what they think they should be doing. First, Gerald Holton in an article on modern science and its intellectual traditions cites some statistics which indicate that the pursuit of scientific knowledge is certainly not the strong or major endeavor that the generality of the model would imply. I will not review all the data, which are available in his *Science* article of March 1960 (pp. 1187–1193) for I think only one example will show the direction of his findings. He quotes a Naval Research Advisory Committee Report on Basic Research in the Navy, dated June 1, 1959, which shows that of 750,000 trained scientists and engineers, only 15,000 are responsible for the major part of creative work done in basic research. The sub-traction makes it evident that most scientists are doing other things."

A second comment in point comes from W. S. Sayre (*Science, 131,* 859, 1961) who tried to establish which scientific group represents the scientists' interests most accurately and most completely, or which of the scientific bodies or members of the community makes and espouses the elements of public philosophy that have become known as scientific philosophy. He found himself unable to find out who were the accredited spokesmen for science. The "scientific community" turns out to be a phrase which though often submitted as identification is a word of uncertain judgments, internal fragmentation and splintering which gives few leads as to how the various groups or individuals or boards or interests are related to each other. While some individuals, or small and relatively elite groups take on roles as leaders at certain times in science's history, none per se is universally recognized by the scientific community as the authentic authority in any policy-making area. Thus, the diversity within groups, the overlapping between them and the duplication of membership and association suggest little of the unity among scientists that a dominant model would have portended actually to be the case. There turn out to be dozens of special organizations and associations of scientists so that literally hundreds of aspects of science are being represented; there are duplications and overlaps, and knowing

191

that no spokesman of any group speaks with a universal voice upon a given policy, or program, every single scientist is similarly split. As Sayre says, "the association of scientists share the pluralistic, fragmented, internally competitive attributes of other group participants in the American political processes—whether political parties, business, labor, agriculture, professions, national group or governmental bureaucracy.

There is a third interesting study which points in the same direction. H. G. Gough asked a group of researchers (not all academic) to describe the kinds of researchers they were.[18] The men did a Q-sort of 56 statements dealing with scientific activity, values and modes of research procedures, and when factor analytic techniques were applied, these revealed eight different kinds of researchers. Some men described themselves as zealots dedicated to research, driving indefatigable workers; there were the initiators who "react" quickly to problems, generate ideas, stimulate others; the diagnosticians, the men who saw themselves as "good evaluators," able to diagnose strong and weak points in a program quickly and accurately; the scholars with exceptional memories and an eye for detail and order though not perfectionistic nor endless seekers for ultimates; the artificers who seem to have a special facility for taking inchoate or poorly formed ideas of others and fashioning them into workable and significant problems; also the estheticians, the analytical minds who prefer research problems which lend themselves to elegant and formal solutions; the methodologists, vitally interested in methodological issues and problems of mathematical analysis and conceptualization; and independents, men who avoid team activities and administrative work and who think in terms of "physical and structural models" rather than in analytic ways.

This means that great stylistic variations in scientific research do exist and can be specified, and furthermore, that within relatively similar activities, the men differentiate themselves from each other—thus indicating fine distinctions and marks of individual identity within the marks of the larger group identity.

These examples suggest that, while our scientists insist that "shifts" from the idealized model are only just coming into existence with the advent of large scale science, it is unlikely that this is the case. More probably, the diversity of models has always been present, with the so-called shifts having always described certain of the researchers. However, their presence was up till now concealed. It seems to me that the present situation in science is serving to expose or high-light a condition among the scientific group that was previously ignored or pushed into the background because it was unacceptable; it was a deviance from the "main models," and thus in poor standing.

It is likely that there have always been scientists who would have been as happy being merchants, who regarded their jobs as comfortable and regular occupations, and who went into the vocation merely because they were brighter in mathematics than some of their schoolmates. They may not be so prevalent on university staffs where academic position depends on producing research, but even here many have probably found their ways quickly to administrative posts. I think science has always had to depend on men with varying strengths, skills and roles—depending as it does on the intersubjective testability for carrying out its goals. Only now, however, when the field of science itself has so mush-roomed that its needs for different "kinds" of men has been brought into the open—and even more—when it puts a pre-mium on the varied resources these men can furnish—can these "deviates" from the old "model" feel they are respect-able and therefore come out into the open.

It seems quite obvious from the interview data that the subjects of this study, the academic people, feel that the training they are giving the young men coming up is inappropriate in terms of the way science is being done. Graduate students get a taste of the independence, the search for truth, the opportunity to exercise judgment that the lone investigator had—but it is hard for them to find opportunities for direct application of these skills. Instead, future work more often rests on interests that training and research have engendered, with the student having to adapt his old ways of practice into the new professional setting. Essentially the graduate student, or the post-doctoral fellow better exemplifies the more idealized picture of the scientist than does any professional person later in his career, merely because research work is so intruded upon by other responsibilities and obligations as one progresses. However, even in the academic setting one finds a greater dispersion of parts among the group than ever before; and an ever-shrinking opportunity for the student to do what he wants to do by himself. The opportunities for individual choice of problems are usually limited; frequently a student comes in at the point where another student has left off and pursues something that the professor has singled out as his field. Even techniques of approach are sometimes strictly dictated by the professors who want to clean up a problem in which they first have made a mark.

Therefore, the laments of the older scientists toward the changing attitudes of the younger probably reflect not only what they see on the outside, but also what they sense in their own setting. Much as they project their blame onto the large-scale scientific organizations, they are undoubtedly feeling some qualms of guilt as the mentors of young researchers who cannot maintain the kind of scientific traditions to which they as students were so dedicated.

The important question, of course, is whether they are needlessly worried and, if the worry is a realistic one, what they can do about it. The answer to the first question can come completely only after the fact. However, it should be pointed out that the field of science itself offers certain safeguards. Obviously the models of the scientist are not unlimited, for science presupposes certain attitudes, actions, and ideologies for the pursuit of research. However, it may turn out to be very important for scientists to establish where the crucial point of correspondence lies between the model of the research scientist and actual scientific progress. In this way, the aspects of modification and practice that could go by the wayside without essentially affecting the model could be delineated. Only trial and error can tell how much modification could be made without betraying the ties to the intellectual; for example, where the compromises could be made and how they could be effected, where the point of no return is for the identity of men before the main aims of science are pushed into the background.

Many actual changes in practice have slipped into the scientific mores without people being too conscious of them or analyzing their effects. There may have been some eating away of tradition and ideals, but had this been extremely serious, it would probably have been more vigorously brought to attention. The traditional professor-student relationship is an example of this: at one time this was thought to be the only way to transfer the scientific torch from generation to generation, the only way one experienced man could communiate his approach to scientific problems. Now it is evident that the relationship is seldom possible, except perhaps at the post-doctoral level, and even here the number of students per professor, and the professors' increasing commitments to other duties, have tended to distort the intimate relationship by which one man came to know and respect another.

As scientists decide what compromises should and can be effected without jeopardizing the essence of science itself, it seems to me very important that they recognize the role of the "ego" in the word "ego ideal." We have always assumed that rigor and hard work could be measured in time spent in research and in the relative lack of other interests—and that these factors were actively reflected in the degree of scholarship, the incision of the scientific attack on the problem, and the brilliance with which a problem was solved. Perhaps it was as much—if not more—reflective of the personal needs, and the psychodynamics of the men who grew up and looked at science in one way, as much as inherent in the demands of the work itself. The men of "old science" grew up in a culture where thoughtfulness, reflection and preparation for adult vocation through the development of inner resources was the only way science—or for that matter any profession—could really be approached. And in our study this is certainly what we have found; that the men as a group demonstrated these characteristics and easily took on these ideals. But perhaps the same progress, the same amount and kind of profit, might have been gained by a number of roads—according to what fits the individual personality best. Donald Michael has pointed out that there are a good many psychological and sociological reasons—to say nothing of the first-hand experience of many observers on the American scene, including foreign scientists—for believing that the whole trend of social values today is, in fact, away from the contemplative, away from the concern with the complex, away from the sense of calling, dedication, and single-minded purpose.[19] If this is the case, then it is obviously reflected in the attitude of the young people who come up. There is evidence of its universality: in medicine, too, deans are finding that students are picking specialties in which there are no long hours, few night calls; specialties which are picked, not because of their inherent interest, but because they promise comfort for the doctor. (To the utter amazement of people in psychiatry, this field is thought to be one of these comfortable specialties.)

If this is the case, and if it is also the case that, to some extent, the psychodynamics of the earlier scientists have dictated the now institutionalized practices of science, then it will be interesting to see the compromises that ultimately result when the men who go into it today, and the minimum requirements of science's methods and goals, come face to face.

Having a number of models of scientists, or at least having them out in the open, essentially gives recognition to the diversity of persons who make up the scientific community. The addition of many models per se will not insure that any single one will be a better approximation to a real scientist, for as we have learned from physics itself, where the existence of two "models" are employed to explain the same phenomenon, theories about nature or men are merely intellectual tools or instruments which reflect less the reality than the ingenuity of the men who construct them.

NOTES

1. This quotation seems to me a good illustration of what many creative persons, especially those in the arts, have commented upon: how their creative talent seems to become almost anthropomorphized for them, taking on various qualitative characteristics and connotations of "good" and "bad." Some describe the feeling that they are helplessly playing out legends or roles over which they have little personal control.

2. Some may view these self-images entirely as ways men have of justifying their occupations to themselves. But as Ortega y Gasset has said in *Man and Crisis,* New York: Norton, 1958, "No one can assume that dedicating one's self to an intellectual pursuit does not need any justification, whereas dedicating one's self to chess or drunkenness must be explained."

3. See Norbert Wiener, "The Megabuck Era," *New Republic, 138:*10–11, January 1958.

4. Cf. H. A. Shepard, "Basic Research and the Social System of Pure Science," *Philosophy of Science, 23:*48–57, 1956.

197

5. See V. Aubert, "Chance in Social Affairs," *Inquiry* 2:1–24, Spring 1959.

6. Ortega y Gasset, *op. cit.*

7. Who would have thought the political atmosphere in Russia would have permitted scientific creativity, of which today's events bear testimony, to flourish as it has? This gives rise to many questions on the relationship between sociocultural circumstances and individual creative productivity. I have wondered, for example, how much the swing toward *Zeitgeist* at various times in the history of ideas reflects man's general feeling of intellectual helplessness in the face of certain scientific problems as well as the cultural forces at play. This is suggested from interview data in this study where one finds that the men who have shown their scientific mettle unequivocally give little weight to the influence of other people or conditions on their accomplishments. Instead they point to their own motivations and resources and their ingenuity for making their scientific fate. In this study, men of comparable age and time in science who have attained lesser successes tend more to weigh outside factors as significant for success. This also suggests that the work on the development of scientific ideas has perhaps not paid sufficient attention to the differences in the degree to which different individuals are receptive to, and even welcome, conditional influences, and the ways others find to isolate themselves from them. I am aware that this may show my clinical biases for, unlike the psychologist Edwin G. Boring, who interprets developments with a long look at the trend of circumstance of the historian, my own predilection is to see man's fate largely as the result of his manipulation of his reality.

8. In Ben Shahn, *Shape of Content,* Cambridge, Mass: Harvard University Press, 1957.

9. These scientists' experiences support Michael Polanyi's contention in *Science, Faith and Society*, London: Oxford University Press, 1946, that science, like all "arts," is best learned informally in the master-apprentice fashion, for a man's labors will reveal the way he chooses problems, selects a technique, reacts to new clues and to unforeseen difficulties, discusses other scientists' work, and keeps speculating all the time about the hundreds of possibilities that will never materialize. This may transmit a reflection of his emotional vision.

10. In one of the West Coast universities it is interesting to watch a European-like center developing at the feet of a notable

scientist. Although it is a graduate department and attracts some already well-established students from all over the world, there the spirit of the old-fashioned work with apprentices seems to prevail.

11. Max Lerner has pointed out one danger of the "fear of geniuses" that has occurred in industrial research, a danger even more corrosive than merely scaring these creative persons away from research units not wanting to bother with them. Those who do go into an atmosphere which is hostile to their "brands" of independent thinking develop their own inhibitions which may completely disable original thinking. His chapter, "Culture of Science and the Machine" in *America as Civilization,* New York: Simon & Schuster, 1957, is an interesting presentation of America's development into what he calls an Enormous Laboratory.

12. In this regard, see V. Aubert's interesting analysis of the roles of lawyers in dealing with troubled persons in "Legal Justice and Mental Health," *Psychiatry, 21:*101–113, 1958.

13. As example, see R. H. Knapp and H. B. Goodrich, *Origins of American Scientists,* Chicago: University of Chicago Press, 1952; and R. H. Knapp and J. J. Greenbaum, *The Younger American Scholar: His Collegiate Origins,* Chicago: University of Chicago Press, 1953.

14. Karl W. Deutsch suggested the distinctions between definition based on function and on inner attitude in his "Comments on 'American Intellectuals,'" in *Daedalus, 88:*488–491, Summer 1959.

15. This is not a new expression. Its first "model" seems to be Benjamin Thompson, Count Rumford (1753–1814). He was a Massachusetts Tory who fled from the Revolution, served the English government for several years, and ended up in the service of the Elector of Bavaria. Under this prince, he became minister of police, re-organized the Army, arresting 2600 Munich beggars in one day and conveying them to a work house of his design. His memorable contribution to science, a study of the nature of heat, was inspired by experiences in Bavarian cannon-manufactories.

16. Personal communication, 1960.

17. V. Aubert, *op. cit.,* has pointed out that the deference paid by scientists to luck probably serves the same function as it does in other highly competitive social structures. It bestows freedom of responsibility for failure upon the daring adherent of the novelty value in science; it prevents failure from being interpreted as a reflection of inability, and it may protect the successful from unbearable envy.

199

18. H. G. Gough, "Stylistic Variations in the Self-views and Work Attitudes of a Sample of Professional Research Scientists," *Proceedings,* Western Psychological Association, Monterey, California, April, 1958.

19. D. Michael, "Scientist through Adolescent Eyes: What We Need to Know, Why We Need to Know It." *Scientific Monthly, 84:*135, 1957.

V I

The Scientific Life Style

IN THE PRECEDING CHAPTERS, I HAVE considered the scientists as a single group, and have tried to search out what has made them one. In this chapter, the orientation is different for their vocational identity will be taken for granted, and I shall use it to see how it influences the other aspects of their lives, their nonvocationally preset roles. Drawing upon the interview data, I shall look at the research scientist in his functions as the head of a household, as a member of the community in which he lives, and as a person at leisure and play.

The purpose of spotlighting the scientist in these ways is twofold: first, to draw a more complete picture of the scientific man—to show that his is not wholly a one-sided existence; and second, to study how his identification as a scientist, with its characteristic orientations and ways of acting and reacting, leaves a mark on his nonscientific roles. To some extent, previous chapters have predicted the directions the data in this area will take: I have shown, for example, how much the core of emotional involvement is centered in work and in work relationships, and thus, it is likely that scientists would demand, expect, and get less satisfaction from personal relationships at home. Also, I would hypothesize from the fact that science has been shown to be a setting which takes on different meanings for different men, that the extra-professional kinds of behavior are similarly motivated by a variety of needs and searches for satisfactions; but, inferring again from the personality data, that each role is compact, neutralized, and neatly separated from the other.

Unfortunately, the data about the nonscientific aspects of these men's lives are not so comprehensive as the work data—again something that could have been predicted. Some scientists were a little reluctant to tell about their private affairs, and some were less skilled in talking about their private affairs than they were about their jobs. In some men, I felt that what seemed to be hesitation was actually repression and impoverishment in these areas. I think, however, that the interview data are sufficient to suggest the circuitous ways in which the scientific style finds nonscientific expression.

❦ The Scientist as a Family Man

THIRTY-SIX of the scientists are married, and all but two of these have children. Of the single men, one has been married twice.

On the one hand, the scientists are examples of the middle-class culture often seen in the university town; and yet, in some respects their outlook and way of life are urbane and upper class. Generally they lead quiet, unpretentious, even-tenored, rather steady lives. They come home regularly for dinner, and spend the time before and after dinner with their children and wives; pursue their hobbies systematically; and, more often than not, spend the evenings reading journals, novels, magazines, or watching television. Most live on a fairly modest scale and do not spend much for theaters or entertainment. Their children grow up in middle-class neighborhoods in which they reside for long periods of time. Some few receive a private education, but most attend public schools. Home life is respectable and comfortable, and one would have to look very hard to find examples of unusual, uncontrolled, or deviant living patterns.

On the other hand, their lives are not uneventful. They travel a good deal, spend sabbaticals abroad, and, to some extent, they develop broad and cosmopolitan interests and tastes; they seek out the intellectuals in foreign countries, and even develop some facility in adapting themselves and their families to new tongues and environments. One scientist in this study took his young children abroad during his Fulbright year, and they all spent the summer camping throughout the Continent, a feat which drew no small acclaim from his colleagues.

Their lives, then, are not conventional in the usual sense, nor are they extremely unconventional. Yet, despite the fact that their home lives are interesting and varied, one gets the impression that these do not reflect their most exciting selves.[1]

For one thing, the interviews reveal that the scientists are not able to give the most significant parts of themselves to home and family. They feel that most of their individuality and personality comes out in their work, and what they as individuals can contribute uniquely is drawn out in studies and laboratories. This is why so much of their sense of identity comes from their professional roles, and, by

203

contrast, this is why their roles at home hold relatively little interest for them; and why they give it in turn little of their best. As a result, their wives and children know those aspects that encompass the commonplace and pragmatic, but they know very little of those aspects of the scientists' personalities that are concerned with the personal and the intimate. A number of men whom I interviewed mentioned that they had never told anyone so much about themselves as they had told me, although the interviews were not so sustained nor so intensive that extremely intimate material was proffered. Thus, it would seem that even the personal is more readily expressed in the framework of science than it is in relationships at home—or at least those aspects of the personal from which the scientific men derive their sense of identity.

Also, the data show that the roles at home and work remain fairly well isolated from each other. To some extent, the difficulty in communicating science to the nonscientist is involved in this; in this respect the wives and children are no different from other lay persons. "What happened at work today, dear?" usually boils down to the intradepartmental gossip, who was at what committee meetings, and a few of the worries about students and funds. A number of men told me how little their children know or understand their work, even though they make an effort to show them their laboratories, and try to tell them what being a scientist is like. They know their children mouth some rather advanced scientific words and concepts, and yet the scientists are aware that the youngsters have little real understanding of what science is like, and particularly of what they do for a living. Some men try hard to give their families some of the color of the life they enjoy, because as a few admit, they are uncomfortable in loving something they are unable to share with those who are closest to them.

One chemist tells how his wife has bolstered his work:

I got married in graduate school, and I would say that I have a nice relationship generally with my wife. She's the kind of person who is a hard worker, and she encourages me to work a great deal. Yet now that we've sort of achieved a great many things, I have the feeling that she herself is beginning to question the value of all the sacrifice. Of course, she doesn't have much opportunity really to think about that because of the children. She herself is a very nonintellectual person, one who has always been that way.

Others tend to compartmentalize their different activities carefully, which often sets the pattern for the rest of the family. It is not surprising to see the isolating tendencies—which they have used effectively at work—employed in separating work concerns from home concerns. And wives help effect successful isolation by taking over major responsibility for the running of the home and the welfare of children. They also frequently become the family representative in all community and school affairs. The scientists find a great deal of support among their academic colleagues for letting their wives take over these things, for this is the most frequent pattern of division of family responsibility in the university community.

Some scientists parcel out the time they spend with their families very systematically. They usually try to give their children a certain minimum of time, plan some "family weekends," and show the same preferences for precision and organization at home that they do in their laboratories. Two of the scientists set aside specific time every evening for scientific experiments with their youngsters.

I was struck with how much pleasure the fact of system and regulation in their lives provide for them. Handling the inevitable emotional pressures of family life logically seems in itself to be a challenge. One geophysicist said:

205

I have for many years made it a general practice that after leaving the office, the scientific work is finished for the day, and I do not take up reading of scientific matters after that at home. I put all scientific things away. I found that it's a good thing to stop at a certain hour of the day and do something completely different. My uncle, a physician, told me very early that when I started to study I should not work on some days, but that I should hike. Also every day I should walk for at least an hour, regardless of how little time I had. I can tell you my normal schedule: Usually about 5:30 or so, I get up, and I get the paper and go back to bed with it, read it for an hour, get up, have my breakfast, leave about 7:00, and start here about 7:15. I work 'til about 11:30, then I drive to get my mail and other things which may come up, have lunch at home, and after lunch come back and stay 'til 4:00 in the afternoon. Though I do not insist on any exact times in the afternoon this routine just happens.

Another scientist, with small children, has developed this home routine:

My time schedule is spent this way: I get up a little before 5:00 in the morning. I do my writing, my reading, my literature work during that time—between 5:00 and 8:00 generally, a very concentrated three hours; then I rush through my shaving, have a very quick bite of breakfast, and try to get to work sometime between 8:30 and 9:00. But if I'm going well doing writing or literature work, I continue it. If it took all day, I'd do it. I get all my ideas during that time. I read, I make notes, and I daydream about the work I'm doing at that time. It's very relaxed, a pleasant time for me. And if it's going well, if I feel I'm developing something and can start writing, then I do. I go on until I feel I can stop, but that happens rarely. Then I've shifted my schedule so that now I stop about 6:00. I figure from 6:15 on is family time. I come home— that gives me enough time to put one child to bed right away. I feed one child, dance with him a bit, and make him laugh. That's very satisfying. Then the fourth child, I don't pay much attention to—he's not old enough. Then I eat supper, play with the other kids, storytelling— that's a lot of fun for me.

Others are casual about it. Some of them enjoy spending the late afternoons listening to their children practice, and practicing themselves, for many have taken up the instruments they wanted to play in their youth. But many confess that they think about what scientific reading they should be doing during that time. A few realize that their time spent at home is largely a not-too-well-rationalized rebellion toward their work. One chemist sees his sporadic efforts in the face of demands for long hours in the laboratory as a defensive maneuver: "I never knock myself out as thoroughly as I should; probably it's an ego saving device by which I keep saying to myself, 'You are better than you are.'" And yet it does not quite come off because while he is painting, sculpturing, writing, and playing with his child, this man is always nagged by the feeling that he should be working.

Most of the scientists work in the garden, paint their houses, take their children camping. Some enjoy these things, but others do them dutifully, feeling they are obligations which keep them from spending more time in the laboratory, which they would prefer. Some are so pulled toward their work that they determinedly, but guiltily, leave their wives with the daily chores, but find themselves doing much more than they really have to in what little time they are at home. Others exaggerate the immediate press of work so that it frequently becomes the excuse for not taking the trips that they are not too interested in, or going to the parties that bore them, or staying at home with the "cats, dogs, and infants."

A number mentioned spontaneously that they knew

their devotion to work kept them from recognizing inter-personal problems that they did not want to face. One chemist described the absence of overt conflict with a first wife with whom he found he had nothing in common. He felt that he was quite unaware of this for a long time because he was so absorbed in his work. It was only when he became interested in other women that he realized how unhappy he was. Another man spoke of a series of relationships, mainly conducted under the laboratory roof, with women who subsequently committed suicide or who died—with no thought of his own need to choose disturbed women or his own possible contribution to their fate.

Because scientists frequently travel to meetings and occasionally go abroad, vacations hold less luster for them than they do for the wives, who look to the summer for a glimpse of scenery that the kitchen walls simply do not provide. Some men describe real "vacation neuroses," to extend Freud's "Sunday neuroses," and literally cannot stay away from work for more than three to four days at a time. Those with wives who cannot stay away from their children for longer than that, find that they have a happy match indeed.

Many scientists described their wives as being bright, intellectual, and eager to use their own talents, although some were dismayed at their own ambivalences toward their wives' strivings. On the one hand, they were proud of their wives' abilities, and aware of how limiting staying at home was. The scientist who felt it his duty "to keep my wife from becoming the nonentity that most chemists' wives are," did stay home with her every evening. The scientist who shared his wife's anxieties about whether her writing talents, which flourished at Radcliffe, would vanish before she had time to give them any real test, took over a large share of the care and feeding of their children, but this at the expense of more time in the laboratory. On the other hand, they were also concerned about what would happen when the wives were half diverted elsewhere, so that the home would not run so smoothly and efficiently as it had. Since their work demands a kind of intellectual functioning that is free from conflict, and from pressing emotional demands at home, the men depend on their wives to facilitate this.

Some scientists realize that they are not too easy to live with. One says, for example:

> I don't let things excite me much. Perhaps it would be better if I did. I don't get terribly excited about anything. I can't get very mad for instance. This occasionally makes my wife angry. She is just the opposite temperament. She flies off the handle just like that; I never fight back. I'm not sure this is the best way to be because I think I miss the high spots as well as the low spots. If something works out well that we've been working on for many months or years, and suddenly I see the light—well, then of course I'm very encouraged, and I feel good for some time to come. But I certainly also get occasionally depressed; it seems like "what's the use" for a while. I think then maybe science is not the right job for me, and maybe I really don't belong here. But after a time, this passes. I don't know how I work out of this. It seems that eventually something happens that's good. I may go home and not say much for the evening, but I generally am not too big a beast.

Another man says that he gets out of his temporary depressions by doing things out in the garage or something at home that is different and active so that his troubles do not "hatch."

Scientists say their most difficult role is being a parent. Some described themselves as being too lax, too permissive; others were distressed because so little of themselves seemed to have been transmitted to their children. A number who had adolescent or prepubertal youngsters were dismayed to find that the children flitted about from one interest to another, and did not become absorbed in anything for more than brief periods. This behavior existed in a variety of families; it did not seem to matter whether the parents took a laissez-faire attitude toward their children's interests or whether they consciously tried to stimulate their children to emulate them. None of the men felt that his children were as intensively involved in anything as he had been at their ages; even sons who were already in adult work were described as having more varied and extensive involvements, rather than selected, intensive ones. Only one scientist thought that a wide range of activities and interests might be good for his children since these might serve as trials or pre-identification attempts at many fields before settling down to one vocation, but he too wondered what would ultimately motivate them into stabilizing their activities.

Many of the children had already entered professional fields—teaching, science, music, humanities—so that the intellectual bents of the fathers seem to have made a mark; but there were other fathers who were disturbed about children who seemed to be late in settling down and who sought work which would bring them the most money. As one physiologist put it:

> There doesn't seem to be any succession of any more of our children pursuing work in science as there was in my father's children pursuing work in the ministry, but I think we at least all pursued work in some field of general social betterment, as against working in business or in some profit-making activity.

A few of the fathers of very young children asked me for psychological tips for training and rearing potential Mendels. A good many children already showed talents of various kinds. The fathers seemed particularly proud of mathematical precocities, especially in their sons. One chemist said:

My child is a mathematical wizard at the moment, but he hasn't really discovered physical science. He shows a lot along mathematical and analytic lines, so maybe there's some hope. My daughter—it's hard to tell—she may be too smart for a girl, but I'm not sure. There is something to heredity apparently because we didn't steer the children, or guide our son toward some one field. He loves mathematics and in fact he asks embarrassing questions of some of the math professors. In fact—I'll brag a moment—at the end of the sixth grade, they gave the class a Stanford Achievement Test, and it turned out they gave him the wrong one in mathematics because he got it 100 per cent right. He didn't miss anything, so they didn't know where he was in math, but they estimated he must be at least in the twelfth grade. That was when he was at the end of the sixth grade. They should have given the test that's up one notch. Math is his best subject. He's just average in English and spelling.

I know of so many cases where the father is a great scientist and the kids don't amount to much. They don't hold a candle to their fathers. Their fathers had it hard or for some reason were motivated—there was something— but the kids don't amount to a damn. They may have the same intelligence as their father had, or has, but they just don't click in a career—but that's a psychological problem.

Here is another scientist's family:

It's an interesting thing to me that my girl has had as much exposure to scientific things as my boy—they've had equal amounts—but she isn't interested in science. She sings very well, without training; has decided she wants to take ballet lessons—she does all that with no trouble at all.

211

She's very good in all physical things and can trick roller skate and ride her bicycle—things like that. She takes a tremendous interest in her clothes and has from the time she was small; she reads a lot; she likes magic; but she's not interested in scientific things. She's interested in animals, she always has pets—guinea pigs, hamsters; she's got to have them around all the time. She's very sociable, the ringleader of the little girls in making a nuisance of themselves.

The boy is quiet and athletically not so good. He always falls over things and cuts himself. He's just a natural-born observer of nature. He found out for himself how to catch caterpillars, and he found out for himself how to find out what kind of butterfly comes out of what caterpillar by keeping the caterpillar until it hatched out. He learned this when he was five, and he has done this ever since. I tried to expose him to the fact that you can be a scientist—that there is such a thing. I haven't taken him to the laboratory to wash test tubes.

I have a feeling, just intuitively, that my daughter won't become a scientist, and I know I won't do anything to encourage her to be one. I wouldn't do anything to discourage her from it, but I want to be sure my children know about all the different kinds of things people can do in life. I knew nothing but science, although I'm not sure that, had I known of other things, I wouldn't have been a scientist, anyway.

I could not help but think, as the men talked of their children, how some reversed their roles, and were teachers to their children and fathers to their students.

As the chemist above pointed out, scientists are ambivalent about what their fame means to their children. Some have underplayed their scientific achievements at home; one told me proudly of how his teen-age daughter ran home and said to her mother when the father's scientific honors were publicly announced, "Why didn't you tell me Daddy was a famous scientist?" This story showed an unusually modest and humble attitude in the father; even somewhat incongruous in the light of his stake in his identity as scientist. I wonder if a president of American Telephone and Telegraph, of equivalent status in his work, would have similarly boasted of his child's not knowing of the stature that he had achieved.

❦ The Scientist as a Community Member

THERE HAS NEVER BEEN A PERIOD in our history when scientists have held so exalted a position. Society looks at the scientist as the intellectual aristocrat, and yet the scientist in turn seems to look back at society through the eyes of the academician.

Only recently a letter about how scientists shy from calling themselves "Doctor" at social gatherings was sent to the Letters to the Editor column of the professional journal *Chemical and Engineering News*. The writer found this recoiling from the hard-won title incomprehensible. Yet this practice is in line with academic tradition. Whatever rationalization scientists offer in recoiling from the title—as not wanting to be mistaken for medical doctors in times of emergencies—overlies the long history of the university man, whose eliteness and aristocracy was often asserted through the overplaying of the denial of any pretensions in regard to this.[2]

It is not difficult to understand the scientists' identification with the university group. For one thing, it is based on actual affiliation—many men take on administrative tasks which bring them together with colleagues in other departments, and which provide an opportunity for the development of mutual interests and concerns. Many live close to the campus, so that home and school are not distinctly separated physically from each other. And a few have children in the

213

university elementary school. But identification as a university person rests on more than duty or proximity. The university group appears to provide the intellectual stimulation that they enjoy and a kind of comfort of recognition for their own work. Although science demands isolation, it provides at other times a kind of intimacy with colleagues that only persons who are bound by similar intellectual curiosities and experiences know. The informality of research work breeds a camaraderie in which the greatest hopes and the worst fears are shared by the few who understand why the great hopes arise in the first place. In his essay, "Scientists are Lonely Men," LaFarge has poignantly described this. To a large extent, these feelings are universalized to the outer and larger university circle, thus their "natural" community.

In the university circle the scientist who is odd and different finds a fairly tolerant emotional climate, because the great mind commands admiration and respect, and because the association of neurosis with genius is still prevalent. The researcher also finds university life structured along the same lines as the society of science, and this defines his social circle to a large extent. A physiologist, only thirty-five years old at the time of the study, describes how his own status in the university determines who his friends are:

> I suspect that I have lived more rapidly than most, that my career has been condensed significantly. It's always been a rapid career; it's always been a condensation of what I had thought of as the normal—so that somehow it seems to me as I look around, and as I see the people with whom I relate now, my colleagues, I think mostly of the people who are about ready to retire. These are the people to whose houses I go, whom I invite to parties, etc., so I'm living a generation ahead of myself; and I have gotten the emotional reactions of a generation ahead of myself. In fact, I've literally grown out of the phase when one ought to be productive in the laboratory.

Another tells of how exciting relationships with colleagues *could* be:

I find parties most of the time very boring, and I hate women on account of it because they always think their parties should make you relax. I go to a party, and it turns out that a guy I haven't had a chance to see is there. I know he's at Cal Tech, but I haven't been in his office, and he's been doing some very interesting work in geology, on the inside of the earth, and I've heard a little bit about a new exciting technique they have, and I say, "Anything new in geology?" He says, "Yuh, we've got this new technique. Listen—we're doing this and this, and this and this, and we're going to find out how, and we've set the thing up so and so." He's explaining the idea and telling me the beginning of the wonderful result they found about the inside of the earth; and some little woman will come over and say, "Now, you two boys shouldn't talk shop here at the party!" We're not talking shop in a certain sense. She's trying to be nice to us, trying to take our minds off our serious business, yet I hate that.

When I was in Brazil, I discovered they have parties, and the ladies go to one room, and the men to another. It's supposed to be a horrible thing, a terrible thing in this country, a terrible insult to the women, but it's a very practical thing because, damn it, the interests of the two are not exactly the same. I don't want to be interrupted by somebody who's going to tell me how I should enjoy myself, that I'm not here to enjoy myself talking to this guy. I like women, but just to be relaxed with. Sometimes I like parties given by graduate students or young people where they come, put on records of rumbas, mambos, this and that, they dance around—I love that. But the parties by the members of the department. . . . At their parties, I have the advantage that people I might meet might have something interesting to say. They don't dance around and enjoy themselves, so what is there to do but discuss

215

something that's fun? And as soon as you do that, the ladies decide that this is too much fun, so what you do is sit around and talk of trivial junk on a low level all evening, and it's very boring. That I don't like.

Some men have trouble finding other scientists who are their "true colleagues"—to use Riesman's expression—and seek these out in other departments in the university. One man said:

We've gone out little, as you may imagine, since we've been married, but we usually go out with medics. We also have many close friends in the language department. In the neighborhood there are no scientists I know of. There is a lawyer. Most of them are businessmen that we know slightly. When we do entertain, we try to mix up people rather than get a full gathering of chemists. It's nice to have a lawyer, an M.D., a businessman, and a professor— something other than scientists. That way makes for a more rewarding conversational gathering, I think.

This, in example, would suggest that scientists may restrict their social contacts to their academic groups much less than do other college professors, for over 60 per cent of all the Lazarsfeld-Thielens social scientists reported that their circle was exclusively a university one, and at the more distinguished universities the figure was about 70 per cent.[3]

University social events can be eye openers, which put flesh on the idols, and often expose their clay feet. This revelation can give one a strange kind of security if the great academicians have been perceived as being both heroes and demons. One scientist has described how ambivalent he and some of the other young men feel when forced to watch and permit the old masters to take the same lordly positions at a game of charades as they do at their desks.

216

The university's support of diversities in private conviction can also be a powerful incentive for binding the scientist to it. This is true in the matter of religion, for example.

Many men were not actively affiliated with formal religious groups, and were content to let their wives direct their children's training. Almost all had had some early religious training themselves, and, in fact, a few had had rather colorful religious backgrounds. One man's maternal family, for example, had come across the plains in a covered wagon to Salt Lake City, and in the days of polygamy his grandfather had what his family claimed was the largest family among the Mormons, his mother having fifty-six brothers and sisters or half brothers and sisters. Others had been indoctrinated into almost every major Protestant group, joining one after another as their families moved around the country. One scientist in this group is an elder in his church, and his wife is the minister's daughter.

These quotations suggest the shades in their thinking about religion:

No, we never went to church. My father was the son of a Methodist minister, and a very strait-laced Methodist minister at that. My father quoted the Bible a lot. He was, in principle, I think, internally religious, but wouldn't have anything to do with the forms of religion. His principles, which he enforced on our family very successfully, were that children should never be exposed to anything about religion until they were old enough to make up their minds for themselves, whether they took any stock in it or not, so not only did he not go to church, but we weren't permitted to go to Sunday school. He figured that this would really be bad for you because here the young man is being subjected to influences which he can't properly weigh and analyze, and he wasn't going to risk that, so he told us that after we got to be sixteen years

217

old we could make up our own minds if we wanted to go
to Sunday school.

Another's response to questions about his early religious
training:

Yes, I went to church as a child, and I still am a church-
goer, not an avid one, but I think there are some fine
values in this. We are a mixed family. My father's family
are Catholic, and my mother's are Episcopalian. There
was no religious conflict in our home. I was really close
to my mother, and as a result I became an Episcopalian.
My younger brother eventually became a Catholic. The
best sermon I ever heard, one of the few in my life that I
think has been excellent, was by a retired Episcopal bishop.
He said that he thought the distinguishing feature of the
Episcopalian way of life was—and I think this is also true
of Jewish theology—that it is one of do's, not don'ts. It is
a more positive thing. I heard this at a rather flexible age,
and it made an impression on me.

From a physiological chemist:

I went to Sunday school, earned my Bible, and things of
that sort, by memorizing verses. Then, in school in
England, we had to be in bed at a certain time and not
read anything unless it was a Bible. For those two years I
read the Bible from stem to stern, so that I could stay up
a little bit longer and be doing something. After that
period, though, religion has not been a very great factor
with me.

We send the girls to Sunday school and we tell them
why. We tell them we think this is part of our heritage,
and they should choose for themselves what they do. So
we send them to Sunday school until they get into high
school, and then they can choose what they want to do. I

think it's part of our background—and everyone should have a chance at it—but whether they want to be formally religious or just believe what they want to believe is their own choice.

This quotation represents a frequently espoused view:

My father, as I've said, was brought up as a Quaker, but this, of course, is not a religion in the ordinary sense, but it is in one sense of the word. When we were small, I went to Sunday school at a Presbyterian church in Dobbs Ferry for about a year or two; then I came home one day and reported to my mother—she told me this, I vaguely remember it—that all the kids did there was fight and that I wasn't learning anything, and why should I go there? So she said: "You don't have to if you don't want to." I didn't want to, and that was the end of it. I've essentially never gone since. I was moderately interested but I just felt that the kids just sat there fighting all the time. They might just as well fight when I wasn't there, so far as I was concerned. I felt if I were going, I should go for some useful purpose. I certainly wasn't getting any religion out of it, I'm sure; but I was interested in the stories—just the factual aspects of it. My own personal religion is essentially nil. It doesn't play any large or small role, nor has it ever. On the other hand, when I was at college, I heard a then great minister of the Presbyterian church debate with one of the excellent mathematicians at the university on God and on religion in general. This man has written a lot of books on mathematics—excellent books—science fiction too. He has a very caustic wit and tends to give the impression when you hear him talking that he was very clever, but almost always this came out in cutting remarks. Listening to the two debate with each other, I came away with the feeling that the theologian had much the better of it, despite the fact that my sympathies were not with him. But he was reasoned and sensible. It wasn't like the

219

feeling you get from reading Darrow or William Jennings Bryan, where Bryan was thundering and a wonderful orator, but didn't have much of a case. Here I felt it was just that the professor was trying to be clever, trying to make the other man uncomfortable, which wasn't the function of the thing at all. I used to go to church because I liked this minister, but it would have been a rare thing for me to go to church this regularly. I'd have been much more interested in why people believed than in listening to some man expound his morals to me—his or someone else's—every Sunday. I've gone to a religious group at the "Y," when a group of students were discussing what Christianity meant to them because I wanted to learn. Most of them were terribly committed to it and appalled at my attitude, but many of them admitted they were much more in doubt.

One chemist said, "The thing that interests me most about religion is why it is such a force in other people's lives. If I can find out, I may become interested in a religion."

Another condition that serves as a strong tie with the larger university community: the middle-class, relatively fixed income of the scientists, which is set up by and large according to university professorial rank. Income level makes it immediately apparent how dedicated these scientists are as educators.

One cannot help but be impressed with the fact that scientists have taken little aggressive action in demanding payment for scientific services. At the time I was collecting these data, a group of Russian scientists was visiting one university, which intensified conversation about the striking differences in remuneration for scientists in the two countries. Our men spoke of the beautiful toys the Russians were taking back to their children, of their leisurely affluence, and of their great self-confidence based on the esteem held for them by the Russian people. Yet few American scientists thought that something ought to be done to close up the differential in income. Economic security still seemed an "impure motivation" for the Americans, or at least no one would conjecture that it would not have adverse effects on their scientific objectivity. It was almost as if our scientists felt that the open embracement of capitalistic morality would be their downfall.

It should be noted that all scientists connected with the university are not professors, nor are all of them in professorial ranks. There are more status differences between them than there are for professors in history, for example.[4] For one thing, there are many scientific positions which do not carry the security of tenure. S. Eiduson has called attention to the predicament that scientists face who are on research grants but do not have academic status. These grants are in effect "Loreleis" because they seduce scientists by promises of immediate economic gratification in ways that conceal the dangers in having one's income dependent on them. Many scientists take research grants for two to five years at a time. They become concerned only near the end of the grant period about what will happen next, and then, in desperation, often grab onto another research grant which permits immediate, albeit temporary, surcease from thinking about economic problems. In the long run, this results in little chance for any permanent position or increase in status appropriate to years of experience. When a move is made from research grant to academic position, the scientist is inevitably forced to begin at the first levels, and this frequently entails an income cut. The scientist whose income has been derived for a long time from the research grant often cannot switch to an academic position, merely because the reduction in level and salary makes this prohibitive.

One looks for historical explanations for this situation

in terms of the conditions under which science has developed, or for sociological explanations in terms of those factors in research climates which condone such practices, or for individual explanations in terms of the motivations of individual scientists, or the motivations shared by the group. I doubt whether any of these singly could offer an explanation. The juxtaposition of motivation of money and research work is now so institutionalized as a polarity that what might have historically emerged from quite unrelated circumstances has now been rationalized as part of the value system that serves both science and scientists. Whatever the separation of vested interests of the observer might once have meant for his observation, this separation now has come to be considered an inevitable condition of performance, though in actuality it may be merely a distortion which has been carried along through the years.

Kubie, in a series of articles in *American Scientist* a number of years ago, attempted to stress the individual psychological problems that may be playing into this attitude of the scientist.[5] However, it seems to me that to consider this exclusively as a personal, intrapsychic problem does not sufficiently take into account how much reinforcement individual psychological factors gain from the fact that they are shared by scientists as a group. I think it is not accidental that three scientists among just these forty told me the story circulated first by Upton Sinclair about Einstein's refusal to take a salary of more than $10,000 some years ago when he was at Cal Tech. Obviously, this aspect of the scientific system has become part of what they think of as their moral heritage. The position taken is not unlike that which is encountered clinically in the problem of moral masochism where the defensive, self-defeating, self-effacing aspects of the phenomenon are extremely difficult to recognize because the adaptive or humanitarian aspects of the behavior are so stability-giving and so esteemed from the societal point of view. This is acted out in extreme degree in martyrs, for example.

Scientists seem to have the feeling that they have to pay in some way for enjoying their work so much. As one scientist said, "The economic problems are part of the fun." The payment for "fun" often takes the form of exacting punishment in the way of "tightening the belt," putting a good deal of thought into stretching the budget, or in tacking on additional work—usually through industrial consultations or public lectures—to already heavily burdened schedules. Occasionally, the guilt that comes with enjoying work too much is expressed in taking on excessive amounts of it, so that the pleasure itself is tempered, or postponed, until an appropriate amount of sacrifice is achieved. I cannot help but feel that the economic sacrifices could not have been maintained so doggedly, or rationalized so well, were there not a good deal of ambivalence over the impulses that are gratified in work.

The scientists, however, do not close their eyes to their impecunity. As one chemist says:

Right now, I feel pretty frustrated about money in a sense —not really because I'm financially conservative; and we do have a lot of expenses now. We have a better income than we ever had, and we are using it. Important in my continuing to be a scientist is the fact that I have always known that if I got into financial hot water—if there were a real emergency—there is some money in the family that I could call on—not a lot, but some. There's not as much now that my father has passed away, for he left everything to my mother—which is fine. She's actually too tight with it with regard to herself, but probably in the normal course of events we'll probably get some of the money he left—not a lot but some money some time. Now I'm sure that this is one of the things that keeps me in science, because I'm not willing to sacrifice everything for science, and I suspect that if I had been in some of the other people's positions around here I would have already taken an industrial job.

Another uses an inheritance for living expenses, saying that otherwise the sacrifice of staying at a university would be prohibitive. A few relate their childhood attitudes about money to their attitudes about their incomes today. One described how it provides some of the things he longed for as a boy:

> Money is a funny thing. My attitude toward it has always been in terms of what I wanted—something I wanted. Now, for instance, I wanted a house; I wanted it badly because we had never owned a house. We had moved a lot, and that must have represented something to me. During that period when I wanted the house, I wanted money awfully bad, and so I accumulated it as fast as I could. I forced a rigid savings program on my wife, and we got a very nice house, and it's all paid for. Once it was paid for, I didn't care much about money. In fact, I recently bought a sports car because we had $4,000 that I didn't know how to invest, and I didn't want to learn to invest it. It would have taken too much time, and I don't like to do things where I don't know what I'm doing.

Many scientists find that money problems divert energies and time from work. One said:

> What I think is happening to me is something that I know has happened to others in our group. It's true particularly in California—I can't say whether it's true in other areas of the country—that young fellows—say in their thirties and forties—get married, have families, and can't wait to get a home. They go out and get themselves a house; and then, instead of spending their nights and their Saturdays and Sundays working on research and developing their careers, they're busy working at home. They don't have

enough money to have others take care of it and to obtain the kind of living conditions that they want, so they sacrifice their work for it. It's not a good situation. It's all a financial problem. If we could all afford it, maybe we wouldn't hire people to come in and do all the plumbing and fixing. Many of us do like to putter around, but unfortunately doing everything detracts a lot from our main vocation. There are a few who devote a lot of time to their work, take their journals home and read them in spite of everything, but it's not easy.

If cloaking oneself in university garb seems to bring inevitable economic limitations, what of the code of living that dogs educators in general? Society views anyone to whom it entrusts the training and development of the young as its morality agents. Their personal lives and philosophies are under scrutiny, and they are supposed to be exemplary models of conduct. On the university level, professors are generally viewed with perhaps a less jaundiced eye if they are unconventional, because society believes university students much less impressionable than younger ones. Thus, the motto, which one chemist expressed as the philosophy by which university scientists live, is: "If you leave students and liquor alone, there is not too much that you can do that's wrong."

This is the general societal code in terms of which the scientists' behavior is perceived, and which they more or less take as their own. But, interestingly enough, some members of their "in-group" are often much more conservative and rigid. Some are ashamed of their "preadolescent colleagues"; some ridicule the "scientific freaks," the men who are "silly personally." These labels are pasted indiscriminately on the sexually promiscuous, the frequently divorced, the immodest, the crusaders—and even on those who spend what is supposed to be their leisure time working around the clock. As one scientist said, "Our department doesn't approve of that," as if the rules of the scientific game were somehow being overstepped. The demand for sexually conventional behavior undoubtedly reflects attitudes rooted elsewhere; the scientific community as a group, however, seems to uphold these conventions. While a few individuals have rejected sexual conventionality, a number of men expressed guilt about their sexual transgressions—as though they were doing something that they, as scientists, should not do.

The distrust of the exhibitionistic and the immodest almost assumes the quality of a taboo. It is more than merely the turning away from the phony and insincere; it is as if there were only certain predetermined ways in which the fruits of scientific endeavor could be displayed outside the laboratory, with extraordinary display being illegal. As might have been expected from the dichotomous attitudes about whether it is legitimate to work at success, there is generally higher regard for the man whose work was ignored by scientists outside his own field until he won the Nobel Prize than for the man who reputedly went abroad to visit the Nobel Prize Committee the year before he received the award; not only the man, but the quality of the work became suspect.

Many scientists feel that outside the laboratory and the study they should identify themselves with the "man in the block," and they brag that "nobody on my street knows I'm a scientist." They become adamant about drawing the bounds of their fields of specialization, and are overly cautious in assuming any prowess at all in other areas.

This disclaiming of anything that smacks of the exhibitionistic has its repercussions for the scientists who do become public figures in the community. I found that there was relatively little sympathy in this group for associates who have become publicly known. The ones who limit their performances on television to scientific experiments are acceptable, but not the ones who become embroiled in public issues. A good many of this group referred to the public debates among scientists on the radiation effects of nuclear testing as regrettable, not so much because of the particular merits of the scientific questions or the scientists involved, but because this was regarded to be outside the responsibility of scientists and beyond the limits of their roles as authorities. Not too infrequently this even reverberated against the caliber of their previous scientific achievements.

This position seems paradoxical, for were anyone to list the basic characteristics definitive of a great statesman, they would invariably be those which distinguish great scientists. For example, the marks of a first-rate scientist are his fundamental honesty and integrity, superimposed upon a mind which is at once facile, creative, and capable of dealing with the most complex and abstruse problems, and a long-established reliance on rationality and the scientific method in which problems are thought through and not easily disguised. It is curious, then, to hear scientists say that such qualities should not be translated to the political forum.

The case for neutrality is not new in science and it now has taken on increasing significance because of its larger and more immediate implications: where the responsibilities of scientists lie, and how much the course of work should be influenced by its possible applications. As one scientist said:

My wife keeps telling me that scientists are not doing all they should because we invent all these things that are going to be the downfall of the world. Well, we argue about this back and forth good-naturedly, just to have something to talk about—the two sides. It seems to me that science has no further responsibility. If they invent something that happens to be dangerous, why that's too bad. The responsibility is everyone's—not just the scientist's—to see to it that inventions are used properly, or to decide whether to make $10,000 Cadillacs or atom bombs,

227

or what is good for people, or what is not. If something turns out not to be good for people, it isn't our fault.

The public position scientists take usually is based on whether or not they see their roles as citizens and scientists as two separate roles demanding conflicting allegiances. In part, too, it reflects some of the disinclination of some scientists for having to respond to personalized considerations and for taking responsibility for others. A conscious motive for some in going into basic science was that they thought such considerations would have no relevance there, as it might have in applied science, for example. But they have found that this way of avoiding responsibility was more fantasied than real. One chemist said:

Having people work for you limits you almost as much as working for somebody. You have to be a model for them, and you have to impose the same restrictions on yourself that you impose on them. You can't get out of that. Also, in American chemistry, it's hard to do something by yourself. You can't really, because the operation has gotten too damned big; and, to some extent, your effect can be measured not only by discoveries but also by how you influence people. You get into questions of how many people you want to influence, and how much—that's another thing. Though I'm paid to influence people, I am reluctant to do this. I never wanted to take the responsibility for influencing people heavily—at least in the formal sense, I haven't—because, well—I don't know why. I assume it's because of the arbitrariness with which I think values are made.

I don't like to take the responsibility for setting absolutes for other people. I don't mind people having their own absolutes, but I hate to give the impression of having them for myself and giving them to others. I've gotten used to this. I've had to. It's been a lot of strain. A lot of people try to get me to tell them what to do, and when they do, I always get resentful and withdraw a little—just as I do from dependency. I don't like it. I withdraw from that, and the best I can do is to help them make up their own minds. I can point out variables. Science professors in general are pretty good at pointing out variables, but they aren't very good at making decisions, weighing them, and coming to conclusions.

Another scientist describes the machinations which he has inflicted on himself because he takes his responsibility to his doctoral students so seriously:

I'm very poor with the students who are trying to do research. They come in; they want to work on a problem. The problems I work on are too hard for them. Also, I'm afraid for some reason that I will waste their time, so I don't like to give them a problem which will end in a blind alley. So I come home and start to work on a problem they are considering and find out whether it's a blind alley or not. If it's okay, then I kind of leave them to work their way to the answer. But I already know where it's going to go, so it loses its interest for me. I don't enjoy that too much; I'm not satisfied with the way I get to these students.

Scientists with more public involvements find themselves immersed in defending themselves from disapproval both from colleagues and outsiders. One chemist said:

I realize I could do twice as much if I confined my entire activities to science, but the combination of the two kinds of work I do seems happy. For me, therein lies the bulwark against criticism. I know that I am criticized by some of my less broad-minded colleagues for not confining all my efforts to science. They say, "You're a scientist. You've got to stick to it." I find that this criticism doesn't bother me in the slightest because I realize that it's true

I don't get as much done, but I'm much better off than they are because I learn more, and I understand more, and I see a part of the world that they don't see, and in that lies my satisfaction. The unfortunate thing is that my mail gets out of bounds. People don't leave you alone if you're in the public eye. They're always getting you to do things. I'll give a lecture here and a speech there, or write this or that. I'm fortunate that part of my correspondence is along these lines, but some of it gets pretty irritating.

Relating to the lay community is not easy for most, and they find that they are not very adept at evaluating and judging their obligations to nonscientific groups. Once in the public eye, they find their roles in the community infringing on the scientific activities that brought them to attention in the first place; they begin to feel like victims of success. Some of the group, particularly those in administration and planning on a national level, do what they can to encourage the recognition of the scientist as an expert, but one man has reported that a good many meetings between scientists and well-educated nonscientists make each group feel that the other is speaking a language of his own. This has made some researchers wary of the spoils of success; only those who see the translation of their activities as part of their scientific responsibilities fight to keep the liaison between the groups open.

Encounters with newspaper reports of scientific achievements also send some scientists in hasty retreat to their laboratories. Here is how a physiologist describes a common experience with members of the fourth estate:

What happens is you tell it to one man, and he gets it straight, and he puts it in, and then it's picked up by other newspapers who will . . . I had an experience at the University of Iowa where I was working with something having to do with the eye, and I made the mistake of having a reporter come in and I talked to him. The next day, splashed all over the *Des Moines Register* was: "Iowa Scientist Discovers Cause of Cancer!" Fantastic! It had absolutely nothing to do with it.

These fellows have their jobs; they've got to make a living; some of them have a sense of responsibility; but for some of them the publicity is much more important. It's too bad because I think it's hurting science, and it's hurting the people. People get the wrong facts about science. When nothing further results, people say, "Oh, well, the man really didn't do what he said he would do, and he never really had it in the first place." So I am worried about newspapers and science.

Reporters are not trained in this field, and they should be. They're never going to get anywhere until the newspapers take a greater sense of responsibility. It's not only in science, of course; it's true of almost everything.

One result is that many a scientist has become as closed-mouthed and cautious outside the laboratory as he is within. Thus, a curious situation exists: in which the men who are the very discoverers and revolutionaries in science appear to be on the surface conservatives, for while the public has accepted as fact what appear to be preliminary trends, they are still concerned with the inherent anomalies and contradictions in these developments.

❧ Leisure and Play

IT SEEMS that one can separate the scientist at work from the scientist at play only by such a mundane criterion as what he does for a living.

Scientists are peculiarly individualistic in some of their habits. They do not look forward to long vacations "away from it all"; often, they cannot bear to be away for very long, or if they do go, they take work with them, so that even the beauty and grandeur of the Sierra Nevadas are in-

231

sufficient to distract them from current work. Some never let science interfere when the snow is right for skiing. They do not merely relax after work, for whether they lift weights or garden, they work at this methodically, regularly, with effort and precision; and in their hobbies, many are dilettantes, in Russell Lynes's meaning of the word. They mentally separate work and play, put very different values on them, and there is seldom any question about which one has priority. Time assumes a premium for them as do few other variables, for as one put it, "Although we cannot all be Einsteins just by working twenty-four hours a day, we do have a better chance of becoming great and important scientists." And they know that the geophysicist who puts in twenty-four hours a day does, in fact, the work of three scientists. Therefore, they are forced into devising methods that will admit play into their superego-dictated work patterns, and, with the resourcefulness we have come to expect from these men, they have arrived at some clever and effective ways to "bribe their consciences."

What they know as the nature of the creative process becomes their ally in this contrivance. The ways of creativity are tortuous and have a large component of the unpredictable and the unconscious. This offers a natural permissiveness for indulgence in nonrealistically oriented activities, in the immature, and even in the nonsensical. There are too many stories about great scientific discoveries nurtured by skillful neglect for anyone to deny that their impulses "may need," as one organic chemist has put it, "an unhampered run now and then." Some scientists say that play activities make them work better and think better:

My impression of scientists that I have observed who have an undiluted devotion to their science is that they're not nearly as creative as those who have outside interests and occasionally think consciously at least about some other matters. This is purely subjective. As I say, I ask myself sometimes too whether my attitude in this particular matter is a matter of rationalization, because I don't like to do this myself. I like to do some other things occasionally and am very much interested in whether this really cuts down on my creativity. I feel fairly confident at the present time at least that it doesn't cut down on my creativity, but my feelings are subject to change.

Others describe periods of change from work as "periods during which we get keen again," and sometimes they interject an hour or two during the middle of the day for swimming, baseball, or tennis, or for a noon concert, or for a stroll through the university art gallery. For many, this change is more than rest—it is a "restoring of creative health." Sports, they say, are "good" and they are necessary if one is to minister to the needs of one's "creative ego." One chemist says:

On weekends, I insist on getting outdoors as much as possible—hiking or working, doing some real physical work, and completely changing if I can. Once in a while, I'm stuck with work I have to do that I resent every minute, and I'm away from it all on weekends. I begin to feel awfully stale and frustrated if I go through more than a week without any let-up, and I think I need to turn to something else to completely clear my mind of everything before I come back. I sometimes think a complete vacation in the summer, for instance, going to the beach or something like that, is very necessary. I go down, I completely forget about everything, and then I come back more or less refreshed. But I get stale and tire very easily, especially with nervous frustration. I don't mind any amount of hard work or anything, but I can't stand nervous tension. Research at its own pace is very enjoyable because, if something goes wrong, you can always start over again—but with people demanding your time from one side or the other and asking you to do things you don't want to do, and your being caught between extremes of things you don't want to do, it's really a very devastating experience.

From the way some of the men spoke of having to "treat their creative egos," I had the impression that they feel this creative potential is somehow dissociated or split off from the rest of their functioning—and that other parts of their personality bolster, indulge, and support these talents. This is not too different, I think, from the way Menninger describes how the "ego" of the individual in psychotherapy separates into parts or sets of of functions, so that "one part" seems to observe and to act detached from the vagaries of the "other part."[6]

The sharpening of sensitivities and motivations by alternating activities does not direct every scientist's attention to leisure-time interests. For some, the different aspects of work that their professional activities entail serve the purpose. The distinction here is usually between work demanding originality, and the more routine kinds of work, such as administration and teaching.

Because there is effort, enthusiasm, and discipline put into the "play" activity, there is little of the "letting down" feeling. The tempo of work is hard to shrug off. One man said, "I work hard, stick to it seriously, become tense and driving, and I need the same kind of hardness and violence in exercise."

The tensions cling, too. One man speaks of the discouragement he feels at times, and uses exercise to get out of these moods. He says:

There are certain things that help a lot—getting a lot of exercise does. It makes these periods much more tolerable. In fact, real violent exercise can really wash it out. Going skiing can. It can just wipe out anything. When I go skiing

I usually don't think about things in the laboratory, but I think about personal things the first couple of days. Skiing wipes out everything, but eventually I begin to think of work again and become eager to get back.

Others let their frustrations out in modern woodsheds, which are usually equipped with electrical tools. One man, who takes his writing as seriously as he does his research, says that by being able to move between two such important activities he "always remains optimistic."

Few leisure activities do not have at least one advocate among this small group. Many participate in sports: golf, basketball, handball, fishing, camping, hiking, mountain climbing. Others read a great deal; some do photography, collect records, play musical instruments; some are carpenters and woodworkers, and gardeners; others write science fiction, poetry, and popular articles. In this group there are some tournament bridge players; two stamp collectors have maintained collections from childhood; two "play" in the stock market; two are painters; one is an archeologist, and there are a few who like to dance and to watch television.

Some describe how they have moved from one interest to another at various times in their lives, achieving some of the horizontal mobility which is so difficult to experience in work where expertness is demanded. One man, for example, says:

I play the guitar rather well. I took both piano and violin lessons at one time. I sing fairly well. I just came back from swimming. I'm getting my arm back into shape from skiing accidents. I've played a lot of golf and tennis. I played team sports in high school, played football, played on the tennis team—a number of different things. In scientists, generally, you find this pattern: they've gotten interested in the sciences early and have become narrow in political development or social development, and sometimes had very little cultural development—and this is particularly true when they didn't come from a cultured home. But as time goes on they start developing these areas and also become pretty good in the sciences. This is generally what happened to me.

Scientists report little of the boredom that seems so prevalent today, and that has become one of the major complaints of people seeking psychiatric help. Play is not their way of sinking happily and guiltlessly into complete passivity, nor do they become exposed to the anxieties that effortlessness sometimes brings. The scientists do not seem to envisage play as providing these things, nor do they seem to want them; instead, they expect play to provide the new challenge, the different task, the experience that offers the use of different personal resources.[7] Play does not imply surcease of activity or less challenge, but rather difference in activity and challenge. The physicist who can let himself go in physics really lets himself go in play. Though this might suggest that there is more regression permitted in play and that this furnished the difference, I seriously question that some of these leisure activities are more regressive or show deeper kinds of regression than take place in really creative thinking, in the fantasies, daydreams, and in the "paranoid leaps" that precede intellectual product. Play seems to supply not a less structured or a less controlled kind of behavior but rather a behavior that provides a different kind of excitement or stimulation from that of work. Not having one's living dependent on what one does in play encourages many different kinds of activities and different kinds of ego involvement. The feeling of rest and relaxation from work, and the "resharpening of oneself," lies in the recruiting of different aspects of personality, the use of different skills and resources and personal tools. The difference in kind is what the scientists search for in play.

236

I have been impressed that what scientists choose to do in their leisure often reflects the fantasies and partially fulfilled gratifications of childhood. Play gives the opportunity for re-experiencing some of the satisfactions of "pure" sensory experiences, and it provides enjoyment with no immediate consideration of responsibility or need for intellectual sophistication. One chemist said he particularly liked golf because of "the pure pleasure you get from the feel of your muscles when you swing the clubs"; another took pride in the precision with which he could carve furniture legs. Play also seems to give to scientists a second chance for the longed-for pleasures of boyhood. Here is the way one biologist describes his turning to the piano:

My playing the piano is in a way a dream. I remember walking along the Vistula. There was a big sidewalk there; this was an occupation that we did with girl friends or without. We'd ride in a boat. This was a regular way of traveling, and coming across was a fellow who played the violin, often somebody I knew. I'd stop there, listen to him, and that was something I loved to do. I wanted to play something in those days, but it was just a dream because I could never afford to learn. I never had a good ear for music so I felt if one didn't have an ear, one shouldn't attempt it. On the other hand, I always had the feeling that the thing I cannot do, I really want to do, and this has happened with several things. So, a few years ago, I took quite a few lessons. I decided to go back to it a little more seriously. It was the challenge in it. I know that music is for people with talent, with an ear, and that I have a rough time in distinguishing sounds, and have a poor voice. But that made me want to do it more than anything.

One realizes how little lag, pause, and circuity there has been between childhood and adulthood for some of these men. Play today seems as much a dawdling with the mysteries and uncertainties as is any kind of experimental work that they set up on the laboratory bench—perhaps more so. They seem to have grown up too quickly, "wised up too fast," to use an expression of Kenneth Boulding's; perhaps their excellent intellectual abilities account for this. In their present stake in play, there may unconsciously be some wish to "wise down again," although they probably realize very perceptively that one "wises *up*," and that one can never really "wise down" again.

It would be surprising not to find a few men who have a great deal of difficulty turning to play, since there is such a premium on hard work. In general, I found that it is the scientist whose work pattern is filled with conflict who is harassed by conflicts in play. The chemist who works in such irregular spurts that he never accomplishes as much as he could, describes feeling guilty when he reads fiction in the evening while the journals lie unopened. The physicist who has to be reassured about his abilities by somebody else, or urged to put his ideas on paper before the challenge in the problem itself takes over, literally has to change environments in order really to let himself play; everything in his home setting seems too confined, too constricted. Others compulsively set out their leisure activities, feeling with Sidney Hook that, "If the development of the powers of cooking, fishing, and roller skating get in the way of the development of the powers of reading, writing, and problem-solving, then the first must yield."[8]

A few fear becoming too much taken with play. One chemist describes how carefully he controls his interests:

I do comparatively little—some professional football and amateur sports, but mostly I read. I haven't been to the movies since I've been back from Europe, I'm sure. I listen to classical music on the radio and recordings. I go out to various people's houses for dinner one night a week, or just sit around and talk—very little in the way of formalized leisure. I'm afraid to get a television set because I know damn well I'd watch it a lot if I did. I really am afraid, because I enjoy watching television, and there are a lot of good things. If there is something I really want to see, I'll go to somebody's house and see it.

I don't read nearly as much as I'd like to. Most of what I read is not fiction. I've been reading *The Books that Changed the World,* which is a very interesting little pocket book. You may have read most of the books it's concerned with, but it talks about Tom Paine's *Age of Reason* and *Common Sense,* and Karl Marx, and Thoreau's *Civil Disobediance,* which had a profound effect on Gandhi, and Adam Smith's *Wealth of Nations,* and Darwin—well, it's really interesting—so I read that. I have all sorts of books going—one a book that a friend of mine wrote in college. It's called *Evolution or Revolution,* a study of American foreign policy. I've read a lot of Russian novels during the last four or five years—Dostoevski and Tolstoi. My wonderful experiences in Russia last year stimulated my interest in this.

Play for the scientists, then, is more than mere distraction, change of pace, amusement, escape from time. All of these elements he finds in work. The ethnologist Marceau Eliade has asserted that "the defense against time, which all mythological behavior reveals, but which is consubstantial with the human condition, we find again but camouflaged for the modern man mainly in his distractions and in his amusements—the real fall into time began with the secularization of work."[9]

In this sense, the scientist is an anachronism in the light of modern conditions. It is legitimate and desirable that he meditate at work, that he follow his whim and fantasy, that he defend himself against time, that he even "kill it"—

this is the scientific condition. Therefore, what play provides for him is difference—the difference in experience, in feel, in the use of different resources and skills. Play is the way he flexes his muscles. It is the way he keeps in mental condition and resharpens himself. It is the way—when he is most remote from his other scientific colleagues—in which he reconditions his individuality, that aspect of all his qualities which makes him at one with them.

NOTES

1. The novels about scientists, such as E. Lipsky's *The Scientists,* New York: Appleton, 1959, and C. P. Snow's *The Search,* New York: Scribner, 1955, seem to have as their goal presenting the researchers in a more human light. They substitute the laboratory and university background for more conventional settings, and I was left with the feeling after reading them that scientists are no different from anyone else, except that they were a little brighter in school. This would seem a rather oversimplified situation if one thinks for a moment that in their work settings these men essentially create—at least symbolically —new cultures and then live in them, while at home they are more the recipients of the culture that is superimposed upon them.

2. O. Mandel's contention in "Nobility and the United States," *American Scholar, 27*:197–212, 1958, is that the American intellectuals have left their intellectual learning behind them because of their ideological antipathy to aristocracy and to being the "elite." He claims they live in a state of amiable schizophrenia: as liberals they refuse to believe they are "any better than the next fellow," but as intellectuals they leave the populace alone, or they revile it while voting in its favor. The true intellectuals, he says, have lost their audience and live in a corner; the others conceal the best parts of their faculties which ought to exhort and lead mankind by serving the public by writing advertisements, inventing new toothpastes, and doing "char-work with their lower faculties."

3. Paul Lazarsfeld, *The Academic Mind,* Glencoe, Ill.: Free Press, 1958.

4. See S. M. Lipset, "American Intellectuals: Their Politics and Status," *Daedalus, 88*:460–486, Summer 1959, for a discussion of

the role the low income of intellectuals plays in their debased self-images.

5. L. Kubie, "Some Unsolved Problems of the Scientific Career," *American Scientist, 41*:613, 1953, *42*:104, 1954.

6. Karl Menninger, *Theory of Psychoanalytic Technique,* New York: Basic Books, 1958.

7. Cf. R. Denny, "The Scientific Corps: A Sixth Estate," *Confluence, 3*:220, 1954.

8. In Sidney Hook, "The Ends and Content of Education," *Daedalus, 88*:7–24, Winter 1959.

9. Quoted by Lionel Abel in "In the Sacred Park," *Partisan Review, 25*:86–98, Winter 1958.

VII

Overview

THIS BOOK HAS REPORTED A STUDY
done on 40 living research scientists in order to see what they
were like psychologically, and what has made them become
research scientists. Because so many mythological and stereotypic personality characteristics have been attributed to
researchers, it was impossible without an empirical study to
tell which characteristics accurately defined them, and which
did not. Stereotyped conceptions of the scientists referred to
so many different aspects of their personality and performance that, in order to test these various aspects, it was necessary to design an experiment that would cover enough of
the facets to be conclusive. The findings, as a result, scan different levels of analysis and look at the subjects from different viewpoints. On one level, for example, the investigation examines the scientist from a longitudinal or historical

point of view, as compared to a cross-sectional analysis of his present functioning. Also, some of our information relates to the scientist's inner psychodynamics, unconscious motivations, and ways of behavior as revealed by one projective test, while other material refers to attitudes and values which are more conscious, more influenced and controlled by his everyday situation. This information is revealed particularly by another of the projectives and by the interviews. Still another comparative level of data rests in considering the scientist's individual psychology, such as cognition and personality factors, as compared to sociopsychological variables to which such elements as self-images or life styles contribute, since they reflect behavior as it is influenced by the cultural, or more particularly in this case, by the vocational milieu.

In my first analysis of data where I considered each area separately, I established the factors that were common to the group, and then tried to understand why a research scientist would be likely to have these characteristics. I assumed that, because the factors were shared by the researchers, these variables had some importance for scientific work, or had some value to the scientist. While this approach has the advantage of isolating these common denominators easily, for each set is considered as a separate and independent group of variables, it has the disadvantage of losing sight of the man who functions as a totally integrated individual. In re-evaluating the scientist as a person now, I shall try to show how these common denominators are related to each other.

First I shall compare the historical data in terms of its impact on the man we see today. In so doing, some of the interplay between overt behavior and some of its unconscious determinants will be evident. Then the relationship between some aspects of the scientist's functioning in a number of areas will be pointed out, so that it will be evident that the scientist is and can be understood within the laws of our usual thinking about personality, and is neither so "contradictory," as the stereotypes frequently claim, nor so complex, that he demands a new psychology for himself.

The ultimate picture of any man does not derive from rating all the factors about him evenly, and then adding up the ratings. In fact, just the contrary is true. Some data appear very relevant to his over-all functioning; others less so. In the case of the scientist, the varying degree of emphasis is extremely significant in understanding him, for some of the factors in his psychological makeup have become dominant and have overshadowed others which seemed less important. Interestingly enough, just these different characteristics which go to construct the picture of a man's total personality seem to have relevance for some of the problems that have become current issues confronting the general scientific community. I refer here to such problems as the recruitment of young people into science, a problem which appears to be intimately related to the stereotyped conception of scientists, and the question of whether the scientist has drifted away from the center of larger intellectual circles. I shall try to indicate the relevance of the findings of this study to such issues.

When we turn to the developmental data, it is immediately evident that the historical common denominators lend continuity to the present psychological adjustment of the scientist. If these researchers are singled out at all at this time, it is for the same reason that they were singled out as children: because they seem intellectually gifted. Their minds were their talents then, as now. In school they were usually good, if not superior; a few were even precocious, although these were in the minority. Their better than average intellectual capabilities brought them their first signs of accomplishment and their first gratifying experiences. From here on, these intellectual experiences were reinforced, so that, to put it in G. H. Hardy's words, they soon knew that if they were to make any mark in the world at all, it would be along these lines.

The history data also tell us what made intellectual facility an asset, what kinds of satisfactions it brought. For one thing, while there was little intimacy between the scientist and his family, those positive ties that existed were apparently related to achievement. The mothers were particularly identified with intellectual qualities, and these became the bond between the boy and his not too-warm, giving, or protective mother. On top of this were tangible rewards, recognitions, honors, praise, and scholarships from teachers and other adults. Even friends often found a place for "a smart kid." Thirdly, these intellectual abilities turned out to be self-nurturing; that is, when these children were physically or psychologically separated from other kids by illness or overweight or ungainliness, the boys found that it was fun and even profitable to daydream, fantasy, work puzzles, solve problems, read, and learn. They found things to do by themselves, and found that they could comfort and amuse themselves, even protect themselves from the "brown studies" that occasionally pervade childhood.

The lukewarm emotional climate in which the men grew up had little of the intimacy, warmth, or close family relationship that we sometimes think is so important for children. In almost half the cases the father was absent or at home so infrequently that the child scarcely knew him; mothers were viewed with hostility, and thought to be frustrating and preoccupied; the relationship with siblings was often tenuous. It was not the kind of environment one often thinks a haven for creativity or for good psychological adjustment. And yet it did not turn out to be so bad for the scientists. It stimulated them to look for teachers or adults who might compensate for emotional gaps with parents—and these associations, in turn, reinforced their intellectual assets. For another thing, it permitted them to rebel when they were old enough to leave home—without too much guilt or ambivalence. They could have gone out into the world as adolescents, and have become delinquent or neurotic. They instead became dedicated, hard-working scientists, men who may have had a few troubles on the side, but none severe enough to interfere with their entering this now honored profession. They came away also with a nice set of "intellectual fences" built up out of seeing pathological disturbances at home that they could neither cope with nor understand, such as an alcoholic father, or even a psychotic mother. Often poverty contributed to the upset. While perhaps surrounding oneself with intellectual fences was not ideal from the point of view of subsequently engaging in long, warm, intense relationships, or in developing a very trusting attitude towards the world, it did make these men able to compartmentalize personal difficulties from intellectual preoccupations; it made them somewhat skeptical and not too trusting of the obvious and more prone to rely on themselves than on what anyone else said or did.

This kind of impersonal emotional climate took its effect in highly idiosyncratic ways among scientists, for, to begin with, it occurred in different contexts at different times to men with different psychological and physiological makeups. We see this from the personality data, for from the many variables at which we looked, there were relatively few common denominators. Rather, the men's personalities ran the gamut of character disorders, of conflicts when there were any, and a vast array of defense mechanisms, showing autistic combinations of the same. We could isolate comparatively few common denominators in personality, and what we could isolate were all focused around work: great emotional investment in intellectual things, a sufficient degree of narcissism necessary to think that what they were doing was good and could only be done by them; an emotional emptying of themselves into people and things connected with work; a sensitivity to stimuli. Even when fears and anxieties were analyzed, these were found to be bound up in conflicts around work, so when they were expressed at all, it was evidently in this vocational framework. Work was motivated by anxieties if these did not become too intense; if the anxieties did break through, this is where the effects were most felt. The anxiety did not come out in marriage, nor in social relationships or antisocial behavior, but affected work performances in the form of difficulties such as psychosomatic disorders, which would be a likely way to rationalize any inefficiencies or incapacities in working, or in doing outstanding work.

In only one way were scientists strikingly similar to each other: in the area of cognitive and perceptual styles, the principles along which they organize and structure their thinking. Here we found a group of men all oriented or set in the same way; to the new, the different; to the fresh reconception of the old; to making new perceptions out of old hat; to new ways of seeing what they had to see, and to new ways of describing their experiences. They were all motivated and oriented similarly; and more than motivated, they were even prone to have built up tolerances to take the kinds of anxiety generated by looking for the new and unfamiliar. They fantasied a great deal, too, thus testing out ideas, solutions, plans (much as they had as children), and they learned how to tolerate ambiguities, frustrations, and tensions. This area, then, was the common meeting ground, so that whatever good aptitudes that they might have—memory, reasoning ability, judgment, capacity to evaluate spatial relationships, etc.—all these were combined in the search for the new, the different, the obscure.

What we see in their cognitive styles is that this is a group of men who grew up as intellectual rebels. They became rebels, first, by being bright enough so that they had intellectual

247

ability to spare and did not have to use their resources exclusively for finding ways to get along. Therefore, they did not have to be too dependent on the obvious or the easy—having found no challenge or satisfaction in them. They also had the opportunity, or possibly created the opportunity, to let their good talents and their "set" toward the new and different come to the fore. It was a lack of emotional support that made them turn more to themselves than to others, and which made them appreciate the intellectual rather than the primarily emotional sources of gratifications, freeing them from the kinds of internal emotional uneasiness which might otherwise absorb their intellectual energies.

Any dichotomy between intellectual and emotional resources in personality is suspended by the data; for the cognitive styles show that intellectual abilities became interlocked quickly and early with emotional and motivational characteristics. All of these, then, operate as a unit. Furthermore, the complexity of meanings and significances that the intellect takes on comes out in the individual personality descriptions; there we learn that it would be much too superficial to try to align one kind of emotional satisfaction or one source of drive to a segment of behavior that, in reality, becomes laden with multiple meanings and interests.

We have spoken of the intellectual rebellion in these men and how this was matched by their breaking intimate family ties at adolescence. Although one would expect that the general tendency for rebellion would be supported by findings in the data that would show all these men as aggressive or unusually assertive or hostile, this was not borne out. Some men are aggressive and forthright, but some are not, and apparently this trait becomes more a function of the individual personality than some of the other characteristics that were singled out as common denominators in the data, for example, emotional constriction or narcissism. Our inability to single out any specific manifestation of this trait in scientific men may also have resulted from the way rebelliousness is exploited in science. Once a man takes on a scientific career, he has, in essence, identified himself with a group whose whole rationale is tied up with intellectual rebellion, embodied in the rejection of old knowledge and a courageous search for the new. Aggression or rebelliousness then becomes a group valued trait, and it is difficult to separate what belongs to the individual psychological armamentarium, and what has become his by virtue of having become a member of the scientific group. This can be sorted out to some extent in the projectives which pick up what are basic personality configurations, and what are secondary characteristics reinforced from the outside; but perhaps the best way is to study the functions of a scientist himself, and try to make some generalizations from the kinds of problems he chooses, the way he will stick his scientific neck out, the energy he devotes to defending a position. In areas where the scientific group does not take the united stand—as in the differing attitudes toward success—the individual characteristics of the scientist also come out. In the case of attitudes toward success, for example, we find that if a man is personally aggressive or able to direct his energies smoothly into competition, or if he can display his scientific wares for skillful personal advertising, he interprets these "sciencemanship" maneuvers as appropriate to the "scientific model." However, the more passive men or the more distant and withdrawn, resist the interchanges that the more aggressive socially adept scientists consider quite appropriate to the scientific framework. There are also the cases, as some of the individual personality descriptions show, of men who mobilize more aggression in nonwork situations than in work; who split off the different foci of aggression in different areas of their lives. And while the psychological tests suggest who would be likely to go one way rather than another, or in different ways at different times and in different situations, only an analysis of life style actually confirms such predictions.

It becomes apparent from the study, then, that what becomes the scientific model for any particular scientist—or the aspects of the model that he takes on for himself—is at least partly determined by the dynamics of his own personality. Yet, despite the variability that is implied here, and that the early history data certainly would predict, the self-images, themselves, seem to have had such a great impact in molding the way the scientist should think and behave, that, once a man goes into the field professionally, some of the psychological findings reported thus far become clouded over and disguised. We find, for example, that the self-representations of the group essentially distort and overgeneralize the personality diversities among the men. They unconsciously foster a "prototype" of the scientist by setting up demands for how a scientist should practice, and by suggesting what personality attributes would be valued for such practices. As a result, the scientist's own self-representations perpetuate some of the fixed and stereotyped notions that exist about a scientist.

In our study, we isolated only twelve main characteristics out of the thirty-four emotional and motivational traits that we tested, and we did not find that the scientists were alike in any specific emotional reactions, or that they showed any specific emotional constellations. Furthermore, as I mentioned above, most of the shared denominators in personality center directly around intellectual activity, such as the main direction of emotional investment, the feelings around self, the ways of handling anxieties and fears and their main contents, the sensitivity to themselves, to their own feelings and to those of others. These traits do not encompass emotional behavior, but they are important features. More important, however, is that they are features intimately related to the work setting and cogent to performance. Emotional investment powers work, for example, and anxieties do so also, if they are not too intense. When they are, work is the first area to suffer. Similarly, where narcissism or exhibitionistic involvement in work is drained, or where the sensitivity to internal or external stimuli is dulled, work would undoubtedly suffer more than any other behavioral area. Going beyond these characteristics, all other personality features that tend to promote logic, rationality, control, and intellectual strength, are also interpreted as valuable for the scientist. More than that, they are attributes of the "mature" scientist. By the same token scientists reject in themselves and in others such characteristics as impulsiveness, personal expansiveness, emotional spontaneity, and intense involvements outside of work. Free floating anxieties are also considered undesirable personality traits. They are inappropriate, bad, and felt to affect functioning in a negative way. We can see the effect of having group-extolled personality traits when we look at some scientific men who have taken on a studied picture of great self-control, and impersonal objectivity. They are men who behave as if they are doing a scientific experiment in every situation, weighing every problem, whether it be personal, human, social, in the same way as if they were deciding what instruments to use next and what these data really add up to. Not all scientific men absorb such group-valued attributes as their own; because, as the data have brought out, many of the men have developed sufficiently differentiated character structures of their own, so that their own needs, drives, and propensities mainly direct their functioning. However, the psychological tests show as well that some scientists' personality structures have not been well crystallized; therefore they grasp these group-extolled attributes as personality pictures of their own. These are the men whose identification with parental figures, particularly the father, has been so weak as to preclude any permanent adjustment; thus they look to the group to provide the kind of personal identities that they need for themselves, instead of bringing into the group identity the strength of their independent psychosexual development.

The question might be raised at this point, of course, whether or not this "prototype" of scientists is in fact not characteristic to some degree of all who go into the group. Perhaps otherwise they might not have been propelled in that direction. This is true to some extent, for there seems to be at least a minimum of compulsiveness in most men in this field, reflecting the kind of self-discipline that the work demands. However, there is a great difference between well ordered men who can show control along with some spontaneity, or warmth when this is indicated, who have tact and sensitivity to know when a logical approach is indicated and when it is not, and who can also enjoy themselves and, at times, be impulsive. In this framework, characteristics of rationality or objectivity become one part of an effective and flexible kind of operating character structure, while in the personality structure described above, such characteristics remain the secondary layer of defenses which are at best the superficial front of adaptability used to hold back, deny, or repress more instinctual and spontaneous behavior. Unfortunately, merely because the characteristics for this latter group of men are so poorly integrated into the personality structure, they are often flaunted openly, and are most visible to the observer outside—a situation which adds to the stereotyped notion that all scientists are cut out of the same piece of psychodynamic, and inhuman, cloth.

There are other facets of the psychology of the scientist that similarly encourage the stereotyped, one-sided picture of him.[1] In his life style, for example, the data show that he generally lives a quiet, serious life much like other academic men. Because this is in keeping with his ties with other intellectuals, it is usually interpreted as merely following along the university model. However, it turns out that, for many scientists, this model is very much in line with what his adjustment at home might have been on the basis of personality psychodynamics alone. This is so striking, in fact, that it seems that the scientist has practically transposed the context in which he lived in many respects and grew up as a child into his life style as an adult. In his present emotional scheme of things, for example, investment in the family runs a poor second to investment in work, just as it did when these men were children. They still spend most of their time alone or locked up with scientific colleagues who speak the same language; psychologically as well as physically the great ties are with work and with other workers. Anxieties and energies get spent and respent there, and there potentially also lie the greatest joys. The work is isolated, serious, relatively free from interruption by outside trauma. This makes for a relatively uninvolved, passive, and inactive role at home. The researcher's behavior at home shows considerable passivity and a willingness to pass on responsibility for decisions about children, economic management, and social affairs to his wife. This is very much like what his father's role was, for in his background the father generally played the more passive and inactive part, while the mother was more decisive about family matters, especially anything to do with children—a pattern of relation which scientists and wives generally mimic. Furthermore, it is quite likely that scientists use the needs of their work as a rationalization for their desires to get away from assuming a more energetic and forthright position at home. Most of them have married capable women who help provide them with freedom from everyday routine and burdens, who can carry on alone when they are away—not too different from what scientists saw their mothers doing; and even in their relationships with their children there is a similarity to their own experiences. While they try to give their children a little more time and attention and interest than their fathers showed them, their children have no place in the part of life with which the subjects are involved. Science is difficult to communicate to the youngsters, and so their children—as they themselves had once been—are frequently left on the outside of the laboratory door, standing with their noses pressed against the glass.

In some areas what looks like passivity in the scientist turns out on closer inspection to be more of the isolation that had its antecedents in childhood. This seems to be the case so far as money is concerned, where the scientist's attitudes seem notoriously unconventional and strange. While the data show that these unconventional attitudes in some men were their ways of establishing an iota of difference between themselves and their parents, in others this was more of the insularity that was derived from their inability to tolerate the emotional pain and distress of circumstance when they felt too young and small to do much about it.

This points to one other purpose that this recreating of the earlier familiar environmental context in present day life seems to fulfill; that is the kind of support that it provides for men who are forced to encounter the terrible anxieties, tensions, and self-doubts that get stirred up just because they have to do original work and have to think in "crazy" ways. Once in science, peculiar thinking becomes the acceptable and desirable way of thinking, and thus the anxieties stirred up with this are sanctioned. In fact, even the stirring up of potential danger, bad luck, and failure are part of the scientific game. By being part of the game some of the usual feelings of disorganization and overwhelming anxiety which necessarily accompany such thinking are alleviated. Further support is derived from having a familiar emotional setting in which to think and act this way—in fact, a setting which essentially establishes a continuity between the situations when the first playing with ideas came into being and to be tested out, and the present situations.

Being in the same emotional milieu which demands no new major adjustment, with the same kinds of persons around, and with the same kind of tasks in front of him, makes it easier for the scientist to think that he is not doing something too much different from what he used to do. He is merely transposing mathematical puzzles and "chess" problems into something that is more serious, and therefore much more worthwhile.

In taking on the scientist's role for himself, the researcher has become wedded to the traditional intellectual community. In fact, so far as these aspects of the self-representations are concerned, the scientists seem to be caught in the exact same stereotypes that the public holds about them. For example, they see themselves as intellectuals, as discoverers of new worlds—worlds which they not only create but in which they then proceed to live. Their work is propelled primarily by pressing "inner" drives; thus the majority scorn "impure" motivations such as the desire for recognition, exhibitionism, personal aggrandizement, pragmatic reward—unless these are inescapable concomitants of devotion to the search for truth. Happiness and fulfillment rest primarily in satisfactions at work, with routine drudgery and administrative matters played down as interferences. In fact, rigor, persistence, and discipline have become institutionalized in their morality code as values in themselves—and the "gentleman scientist" is looked upon as a laggard who is bound to be unproductive. These facets of identification emphasize how isolated the researcher is and how different from the general cultural pattern; but in these regards he assures many of the elements that would establish bonds between him and other intellectuals. In fact, he is concerned about the break with the intellectual community which comes out in some of the aspects of his identity which are in the process of change (and incidentally, in those areas where

255

some of the most highly stereotyped conceptions about scientists are giving way).

Changes of self-image which concern these subjects who are trained in "old science" seem to have been most stimulated by the differences that have emerged in the way science is practiced, and the attitudes and values that have accompanied these recently defined differences. An example of the change is the researcher's shying away from identification with forefathers who were "great but maladjusted," or "eccentric" scientists. Reverence for forefathers whose outstanding minds were sometimes housed in odd personalities still exists, yet the new scientists seem to be consciously dissociating themselves from peculiar and difficult associates or students, knowing full well that they may be thus shunting off some very creative workers from their own laboratories. They prefer to depend for progress on well-organized, smooth-running, large-scale operations whose stability demand the minimum of interpersonal relationships—especially disturbed ones. Even colleagues who "play expert" in nonscientific fields and attempt to apply scientific knowledge to cultural problems are frowned upon, and often their scientific work is looked upon with suspicion. Another change comes in the new interest in "putting breakthroughs across." While these men still stress that the main motivation of science is the gaining of understanding and knowledge without concern for its immediate application, they feel that the fruits of their search can be more readily taken advantage of if they adopt the skills of sciencemanship. Some think manipulation of success in science is a natural sequence, if one realistically acknowledges that the same gamut of motivations which are found in other workers is also present in them—jealousy, competition, the desire to please a superior. The new model of science, which is a corporate one, gets much of the blame. With this and with its spelling out of all the multiple subparts, budgets, personnel, and administrative details, comes an increasingly tight definition of what each scientist specifically does at work. Scientists trained in "old science" feel that this is an important change in the view of their role, which has characteristically been in part ambiguous and indefinite, hinting at the possibility of multiple choices. Many scientists have clung to this ambiguity because it seemed to them to mirror some of their attitudes toward the intellectual problems with which they grappled, their dissatisfactions with the obvious, and with conventional ways of seeing reality.

It would seem theoretically, at least, that here C. P. Snow, Ashby and some of the other sociologists of science who are anxious about the growing schism between the intellectual and the scientist verbalize the concerns of our researchers. However, our data show that, in many respects, even these men of "old science" were already distinctly divorced from the larger intellectual community. When we look at their own aspirations, and at their ideal picture of the scientist—the achiever, the creator who draws his strength from being tied to tradition, but who maintains individual identity by breaking from it, it is evident that all these suggest a single framework and a highly specified definition of what the intellectual is like. The great reverence for dedication and devotion, the suspicion of the overly quick success, the ambivalence about manipulating or exploiting their intellectual talents, indicate that these researchers think about the intellectual man in a highly stylized way. More specifically, scientists conceive of themselves almost exclusively in the framework of their own research work. They do not identify with the larger intellectual community, nor are they particularly affiliated with the interests of those outside their own scientific sphere. Few of them explore the continuity that exists between what they do and have been doing, and what other intellectuals do. Even their models are only models while they are doing scientific work, for even the great Einstein was not emulated when he made what were considered "politically tinged" pronouncements. Scientists who have become public servants are thought to have strayed from the research fold. Therefore, researchers have, in general, restricted their roles, duties, and responsibilities to their own fields; thus fixating on becoming better specialists, more competitive, more imaginative, but only in their own areas of expertness. Once outside this area, even this group of tradition bound men have felt that they must be like every other citizen, rather than like intellectual citizens. In this role, they seem to have wanted to cast off their garb as intellectuals and melt into a rather nonintellectual atmosphere instead.

A look again at their life styles confirms this, for to a large extent their nonscientific life resolves around one thing only—the promoting of scientific creativity. This is a rationalization for play, for the kind of role they take at home, the way they apportion their time. The scientist has one main orientation and his style of living is built around it; and vice versa, how he lives, and why, is understood and rationalized in terms of what it contributes to his scientific success and what it might detract from it. Furthermore, a relatively small group seems to have developed intellectual hobbies or pursuits. Even their reading tends to be generally centered around their work or around the more popular magazines and books. A few have artistic or musical interests, but again these men have not identified with, or even become informed about, the mainstreams of artistic or intellectual thinking outside of their own science. Only a few of the researchers in this group—and these are all men who have been recognized for the highly significant contributions that they have made in their own fields—seem to feel that they can extend themselves emotionally, not to mention physically, into the larger intellectual sphere of humanity without actually withdrawing time, energies and efforts from their work. Once having made a name for themselves they feel they can branch out. Therefore, to some extent, their life style belies their concern about how recent developments in science have stimulated a new break with other intellectuals.

This furthermore highlights the curious situation whereby being a research scientist and taking on self-images and badges, has theoretically put a man into the intellectual arena; but at the same time it has demanded that he practice his work in such a way that he essentially has been cut off from the larger community. He has neither had the stimulus to involve himself in the broader intellectual horizons, nor have the mores and practices of science actually permitted him to branch out in his thinking without making him feel he would jeopardize his position in his own field. Therefore, science has at one and the same time lured the man into an intellectual field, but once there, has dictated and circumscribed a kind of intellectual functioning for him.

Thus the paradox: that out of the great diversities of background and personality structure that was apparent in this group of scientists at first look, we arrive at a highly defined picture of the scientist, a picture that is so much defined by the role and identity that he has taken as scientist, that it essentially has blanketed the kind of variety and individual difference that characterized the group initially. We see, furthermore, that men who were interested in literature and music and art, in culture and humanities, have had so little opportunity to capitalize upon these interests once they became scientists, that essentially they have cut off the strings that have made them one with the larger intellectual community.

There seems to me one break in the story, however, that foretells a different fate for tomorrow's scientist. Here I look to the gentleman scientist or the man of new science who is generally regarded as a maverick. Because these men feel that science can be practiced differently without deleterious effects on the kind of progress it makes, or on the rate at which it progresses, or on the genuine inner intellectual motivations of the man, there is a faint chance that they will find time to cultivate the kinds of interests and concerns which will give them scope, and stimulate them to think about the significance that their contributions to scientific knowledge holds for knowledge as a whole. Looking at a few of these "gentlemen" who have wended their way into this study, we learn that they have found time to pursue art, literature, music, and even psychology, after hours. They admit that this demands a kind of compartmentalization of interests that at first glance is antithetical to any merging of one intellectual field with another, but they add further that at least these merge in a single man and in a single mind, where the bounds of time and space can be recognized as artificial and even inappropriate limitations. It is quite possible that, by this circuitous way, scientists will get back into the intellectual forefront of civilization, a position which, until now, their being "scientific intellectuals" has forced them to abrogate.

I want to deal with one final issue to which this empirical study is relevant: the problem of recruiting young people into science, for it is evident that while some of the notions about scientists have been altered in recent years, they are still depicted in a highly patterned, stereotypic way. Furthermore, the studies recently done on attitudes toward the stereotype reveal that very few young people want to take up the researcher's tools in their own hands.[2] For them the scientist is still outside the psychologically palatable pale. He remains a contradictory and puzzling image because his values are not completely conventional; and while no longer an eccentric, he is not a "good Joe." His brain is intimidating, and he seems to represent a worldiness in a world that has a vocabulary that is so autistic that there is little hope that he can ever communicate easily on intimate and commonplace things.

Also, he appears dull and foolish for working so hard. To the young people whose experiences are extensive rather than intensive, who look for things that are constantly stimulating and revitalizing, who have been brought up in milieus which have been built to deliver a continuous series of small but immediate gratifications, the scientist's world seems old-fashioned and uninteresting. Or, if the world is not, at least the approach of the scientist today is, for his practices seem out of tune with the times (even though, to a large extent, his practices have made the times). This attitude does not seem peculiar to science, nor it is completely unrealistic; for as Rene Dubos pointed out recently in an address at the 1961 American Orthopsychiatric Meetings, the changes in social and cultural evolution have been so rapid that today's children can no longer learn from the experience of their fathers; the fathers' experiences are just not applicable to the world and to the situations with which they are confronted.

Perhaps by knowing something about what makes a scientist we can more intelligently decide whether or not the differences in the times and in the social cultural milieu can be taken into account and compensated for. We have learned from this study that there is no one factor in background or experience that is a raison d'être for the man who wants to go into this work. We have learned, too, that certain outlooks toward the world, certain ways of thinking and perceiving, and a high degree of emotional investment in intellectual things, are essentially sufficient to orient the youngster with at least high average intelligence into science. From the study it is also evident that even today's researchers are very different from each other in personality, emotional behavior

261

and in motivation, and that only their being in science has tended to make them look as similar to each other as they do. Neither common experiences nor suitable teachers nor certain conditions present in home life seem crucial to the decision about going into scientific work.

Perhaps even more instructive from the study, and more encouraging, is learning that, in some of the more crucial features of personality makeup and cognitive characteristics, the scientists are actually quite like many of the children today. Our findings show, for example, that the subjects look for the novel, the new, the interesting in their thinking; they are oriented toward rejecting the obvious, the hackneyed; that they quickly tire of the usual in everyday ways of seeing reality. But there is one big difference between today's children and these men that lies in the fact that the subjects try to see how their desire and search for something new and different can be used to advantage in science. The first part of the picture we do see in today's children who are frequently accused of being interested in the gimmick, the novelty, who reject the mundane, who arrive at quick satiation points, and who pooh-pooh conventional attacks and attitudes. Unquestionably, however, they have fallen behind in the second part—the redirecting of any of these cognitive attitudes in any way. The intellect, intellectual talents, interests, and goals have not held out enough promise to them as resources for consistent and increasing kinds of satisfactions—so that what "rebelliousness" they show has not been directed into any kind of work. Nor have any of the other aspects the scientist's needs—judgment, reasoning power, persistence, the ability to tolerate anxiety and ambiguity—been given sufficient attention in their development. Nor has science attempted to show what possibilities it offers of combining these kinds of "cognitive and emotional preferences" for, first, an adult and mature work setting and, second, in a scientific framework that, through its methods and techniques, provides the basis for judgment, logical analysis, and rational approaches that can direct and siphon the rebelliousness into something important, worthwhile, and even idealistic.

Instead of holding out promises to the young people that they will find security, pleasant group atmospheres for scientific work, and personal comforts in science, and thus competing on the same level as one does for students in business, engineering or teaching, it seems to me that science should attempt to stimulate and exploit the active, if not latent, rebellious and absorbing drives in young people; and hold out science as offering intellectual controls for such energy and some potentiality for exploitation. I would not disown "the scientific discoverers," but rather revitalize them; and instead of making the "models" similar to the models in other vocations, I would capitalize on their healthy difference. In a sense I think that youngsters today are not too different in emotional climate or family background from the group that I studied; for the latter has some of the same looseness and family identification, the break from strong and directing emotional ties that seems to be the case now. However, the stability and resourcefulness derived from intellectual talents and the development of intellectual abilities has not gone along concomitantly in today's youngsters, so that some of the most obvious avenues, the most conventional ones that seem potentially to offer the most direct security, are the ones that they seem to reach out for. Yet one is struck by the fact that many of the youngsters who try this, and who have adopted quick closures with obvious gratification, find that they do not get the fantasied security or the same kind of continuity with childhood experience, but instead find themselves grasping for one thing and getting the opposite—and thus disappointments and emptiness are not long to follow.

This study has put great stress on the cognitive orientation of researchers and the way in which it is implemented by additional emotional supports from personality propensities. In fact, the data are so striking in this direction that from the point of view of recognizing scientific talent early, it would seem important to try to validate this on a larger scale. While the ways of thinking and perceiving in this study are derived from individual Rorschach and T.A.T. projective tests, it would not be too difficult to find ways of tapping and evaluating these same characteristics through nonprojective tests which are easily quantified and more suitable for group administration. At the present time, a number of psychologists working in the fields of intellectual aptitudes have developed measures which hold promise of being reliable indicators of scientific creativity. However, they have not taken sufficient account of the motivational properties that these aptitudes take on—something that this study has shown to be very important and intimately linked up with the frittering away of great abilities in students who are poorly directed, insufficiently stimulated, never encouraged. Were such tests administered to grammar school students on a national scale early enough, the ones who had the ability, as well as the stylistic thinking characteristics and motivations conducive to scientific work, could be identified. Then a concerted effort could be made to provide them with the kinds of experiences that would reinforce these attributes and so show their promise as major resources of personal satisfaction. Furthermore, appropriate information about science and its potential for continuing and enhancing such gratifications could be presented.

The external status differentials like money, hours, and effort that are now thought to be the great barriers between science and other professions would, it seems to me, tend to dwindle in significance. Focus on them at this time comes from the fact that the meeting of inner determined need and the external realities of science seems worlds apart; a situation which magnifies the obvious external differences in science from other fields. It should be noted, however, that from a realistic point of view these externals are no longer so large, as Bentley Glass points out in his article, "The Academic Scientist—1940–1960."[3] Once we know that the difference does not lie in these factors, the magnifying instrument must invariably be turned to look at the "internals."

If we really believe that the great scientific drive is tied up with internally directed motivations, with intellectual ties, and with a trust in intellectual tools for solving problems, it seems to me that it would be a mistake to hold out the external features of science—or changes in these external features—as the bait for the young student. The student who grabs on to these as motivation will find that science does not hold out anything which distinguishes it from any other kind of work, anything particularly exciting or unique, and he will soon lose his spirit for it. When this happens, a vapidness will take over the field of science also.

NOTES

1. The difficulty in knowing what the scientist is like as a person is even reflected in modern-day fiction. Except for C. P. Snow and E. Lipsky who have introduced researchers as heroes, scientists appear in very few novels. Occasionally books on university life include college professors who turn out to be scientists, but there the personality picture is exclusively drawn after the academic role. This may be because, as Mary McCarthy has pointed out in a recent *Partisan Review* article (March–April 1961), novelists tend to evade involvement with today's characters; and thus when depicted in story these characters come out less as people than typed caricatures. Although novelists may be unable (or afraid) to draw the scientist as man, apart from the professional work, I wonder whether they appreciate the fact that for most of the scientists the picture of him at work is the man, that the major aspects of his identity come from and are known in his role at work.

2. See, as examples, Margaret Mead and Rhoda Metraux, "Image of the Scientist among High School Students," *Science, 126*:384,

1957; D. C. Beardslee and D. D. Dowd, "The College-Student Image of the Scientist," *Science, 133*:997, 1961; H. Remmers, *The American Teen Ager.* Indianapolis: Bobbs-Merrill, 1957.

3. B. Glass, "The Academic Scientist 1940–1960," *Science, 132*:598, 1960.

APPENDIX

I

Rating Scale

Form CA-L

INSTRUCTIONS:

Please encircle the number in each item which best describes the subject from his Rorschach and Thematic Apperception Tests. You are to study both test protocols together and make one rating for each item based on your consideration of both tests. The numbers range on a continuum from one to five, with one being equivalent to "minimal, not at all, or very seldom" and five implying "maximum, to a great degree, most of the time." If you feel on any item that you have rated it only because you have been forced to make a rating and that this rating is arbitrary and based on little in the test data, please indicate this by *also* encircling the question mark at the end of the numbers for that item.

1. Shows strong capacity for sensuous gratification. (56, 82)   1 2 ③ 4 5 ?

2. Looks for indirect or "neutralized" ways to express aggression. (47)   1 2 3 4 5 ?

3. Has feminine-passive psychosexual orientation. (67)   1 2 3 4 5 ?

4. Displays flexible and mobile thinking, rather than highly or rigidly patterned. (32)   1 2 3 4 5 ?

5. Strong exhibitionistic needs and desires for recognition are tied in with achievement. (67)   1 2 3 4 5 ?

6. Seeks out delicate and subtle impressions. (64, 56)   1 2 3 4 5 ?

7. Prefers complex rather than simple ideas and situations. (3)   1 2 3 4 5 ?

8. Values productive achievement as an end in itself.   1 2 3 4 5 ?

9. Seems to be strongly self-directed and self-disciplined. (64)   1 2 3 4 5 ?

10. Uses parental ideals to set own goals. (82)   1 2 3 4 5 ?

11. Can tolerate ambiguities in the perceptual area. (24, 88)   1 2 3 4 5 ?

12. Works more originally with somewhat structured rather than more unstructured situations. (91)   1 2 3 4 5 ?

13. Shows heightened ambivalent conflicts. (82)   1 2 3 4 5 ?

14. Has strong emotional leanings for intellectual activity. (88)   1 2 3 4 5 ?

15. Prefers to express emotion within intellectual framework, rather than directly. (82)   1 2 3 4 5 ?

16. Is sensitive to moods and feelings of others.   1 2 3 4 5 ?

17. Uses inner resources (rather than looking to external environment) to handle anxiety.   1 2 3 4 5 ?

18. Accepts reality but sees it in a way different from others. (88)   1 2 3 4 5 ?

19. Is so bound by his need to meet the demands of reality that he is restricted. (46)   1 2 3 4 5 ?

20. Fears mediocrity in performance.   1 2 3 4 5 ?

21. Seeks to depart radically in his expressions and thinking from the usual, obvious, or hackneyed.   1 2 3 4 5 ?

22. Value system strongly determined by prevailing cultural standards. (56)   1 2 3 4 5 ?

23. Can loosen or relax controls in thinking without personality disorganization. (43, 46)   1 2 3 4 5 ?

24. Shows richness in symbolic and descriptive expression and association.   1 2 3 4 5 ?

25. Has bisexual tendencies. (26, 82)   1 2 3 4 5 ?

26. "Gregarious" intellectual development with diversity of interests.   1 2 3 4 5 ?

27. Strong ego-involvement and conflict expressed in work. (27)   1 2 3 4 5 ?

28. Detached from strong desires for direct self-gratification. (67)   1 2 3 4 5 ?

29. Shows unusual emphasis on the elaboration of fantasy. (27)   1 2 3 4 5 ?

30. Motivated by a desire to master or interpret natural forces or reality. (38)   1 2 3 4 5 ?

31. Can convey experiences or feelings so that another's emotional response is aroused. (88)   1 2 3 4 5 ?

32. Is sensitive to his internal environment, needs, wishes, desires. (82)   1 2 3 4 5 ?

33. Is prone to depression or mood swings. (9)   1 2 3 4 5 ?

34. Ways of emotional expression are flexible and diversified. (88)   1 2 3 4 5 ?

35. Works primarily to provide internal

271

satisfactions, with little regard for the product. (27)   1 2 3 4 5 ?

36. Has broad time-perspective and strong orientation to the future. (88)   1 2 3 4 5 ?

37. Curiosity likely to be prominent determinant of work. (54)   1 2 3 4 5 ?

38. Interests point to the theoretical and abstract rather than the practical and realistic. (88)   1 2 3 4 5 ?

39. Values work primarily as permitting expression of inner personality. (69)   1 2 3 4 5 ?

40. Imitates and depends on others in thinking and actions. (5)   1 2 3 4 5 ?

41. Productivity tied up with superego demands. (82)   1 2 3 4 5 ?

42. Tends to be highly introspective, reflective about sex. (47)   1 2 3 4 5 ?

43. Is responsive to sensory experience-data. (64, 56)   1 2 3 4 5 ?

44. Has capacity for recombining, reorganizing usual conceptions. (32)   1 2 3 4 5 ?

45. Is challenged by frustration and anxiety-producing situations rather than being overwhelmed by them. (9)   1 2 3 4 5 ?

46. Can easily establish a multiplicity of identifications.   1 2 3 4 5 ?

47. Displays novelty in ideational activity. (105)   1 2 3 4 5 ?

48. Work is likely to infuse or determine his entire mode of living, rather than being split off.   1 2 3 4 5 ?

49. Has a need to integrate internal and external experiences in a comprehensive way. (38)   1 2 3 4 5 ?

50. Desires strong and intimate interpersonal relationships.   1 2 3 4 5 ?

NOTE: The numbers in parentheses refer to studies listed in the bibliography from which the items were drawn. A few items, however, were drawn from material not listed in the bibliography—e.g., item 8, from C. W. Mills, *White Collar*, New York: Oxford, 1951; item 16, from G. Bychowski, "From Catharsis to Work of Art," in G. Wilbur and W. Muenstberger (Eds.), *Psychoanalysis and Culture*, New York: Int. Univers. Press, 1951; item 17, from H. Rorschach, *Psychodiagnostics*, Berne: Huber, 1942; M. Prados, *Rorschach studies on artists-painters. Rorschach Res. Exch.*, 1944, *8*, 178–183; item 20, from the same Prados study; item 21, from the same Rorschach study; item 26, from J. Schimek, *Creative Originality: Its Evaluation by the Use of Free Expression Tests.* Unpublished doctoral dissertation, University of California at Berkeley, 1954; item 24 from the same Bychowski study; item 26 from M. Wertheimer, *Productive Thinking*, New York: Harper, 1945; item 35, from Bychowski; item 40, from Schimek; item 44, from Wertheimer; item 45, from P. Schilder, *Medical Psychology*, New York: Int. Univers. Press, 1953; item 46, from Bychowski; item 48, from Mills; item 50, from Rorschach.

II

Results of Comparison of Groups of Subjects in Creative Fields[a]

Variable Tested	N	Median	χ^2	df	p Level
Difference among populations[b]	65	154	9.208	2	.01*
Artists I	25	162			
Businessmen	25	142			
Artists II	15	162			
Difference between groups[c]	80	159	1.253	1	.30†
Artists (1 + II)	40	162			
Scientists	40	156			
Difference between groups	65	150	8.748	1	.01†
Businessmen	25	142			
Scientists	40	156			

[a] Statistic employed: Mood's analysis of variance (simple) by medians. The formula is as follows:

$$\chi^2 = \left[\frac{N(N-1)}{a(N-a)} \sum_{i=1}^{r} \frac{1}{n_i} \left(m_i - \frac{n_i a}{N} \right)^2 \right]$$

where N = combined frequency or total number of cases in all groups; $a = \frac{N}{2}$ if N is even or $\frac{N-1}{2}$ if N is odd; m_i = number of cases in group i exceeding the grand median of all groups pooled; n_i = number of cases in group i; and r = number of groups. This quantity is distributed as χ^2 with $r-1$ df. (A. M. Mood, *Introduction to the Theory of Statistics*, New York: McGraw-Hill, 1950).

[b] For description of this study, see Bernice T. Eiduson, "Artist and Non-artist: A Comparative Study," *Journal of Personality, 26:* 13, 1958.

[c] For report on these data, see Bernice T. Eiduson, "Artist and Research Scientist: A Comparative Study." *Proceedings,* American Psychological Association, Washington, D.C., September 1958.

* For 2 df, p .01 = 9.21.
† For 1 df, p .01 = 6.63; p .30 = 1.07.

274

III

Items Differentiating between Artists and Businessmen According to Major Areas of Variables[a]

Thinking and Perception Variables

A. Items achieving a significance level of .01 or smaller:[b]

26. "Gregarious" intellectual development with diversity of interests.

29. Shows unusual emphasis on the elaboration of fantasy.

43. Is responsive to sensory experience data.

[a] The 5-point rating scale was divided into 2 dichotomous variables by placing the ratings 1–2–3 in one cell and 4–5 in the other. The decision to place the rating "3" with the first two numbers was made after individual consultation with the judges, who unanimously suggested this alignment.

[b] The measure of contingency applied was Chi square which was corrected by the Yates correction:

$$X^2y = \frac{([ab - bc] - N/2)^2 N}{(a+b)\ (a+c)\ (b+d)\ (c+d)}$$

For 1 df, $\chi^2 = 3.84$ for a level of significance of .05, or 2.71 for a level of significance of .10.

21. Seeks to depart radically in his expressions and thinking from the usual, obvious, or hackneyed.

24. Shows richness in symbolic and descriptive expression and association.

38. Interests point to the theoretical and abstract rather than the practical and realistic.

23. Can loosen or relax controls in thinking without personality disorganization.

44. Has capacity for recombining, reorganizing usual conceptions.

B. Items achieving a significance level of .02 to .05:

47. Displays novelty in ideational activity.

18. Accepts reality but sees it in a way different from others.

C. Items achieving a significance level of .05 to .10:

7. Prefers complex rather than simple ideas and situations.

6. Seeks out delicate and subtle impressions.

11. Can tolerate ambiguities in the perceptual area.

D. Nonsignificant items:

4. Displays flexible and mobile thinking, rather than highly or rigidly patterned.

12. Works more originally with somewhat structured rather than more unstructured situations.

19. Is so bound by his need to meet the demands of reality that he is restricted.

Emotional Variables

A. Items achieving a significance level of .01 or smaller:

31. Can convey experiences or feelings so that another's emotional response is aroused.

16. Is sensitive to moods and feelings of others.

B. Items achieving a significance level of .05:

32. Is sensitive to his internal environment, needs, wishes, desires.

42. Tends to be highly introspective, reflective about sex.

1. Shows strong capacity for sensuous gratification.

C. Items achieving a significance level of .10:

45. Is challenged by frustration and anxiety-producing situations rather than being overwhelmed by them.
40. Imitates and depends on others in thinking and actions.
14. Has strong emotional leanings for intellectual activity.
2. Looks for indirect or "neutralized" ways to express aggression.
46. Can easily establish a multiplicity of identifications.

D. Nonsignificant items:

3. Has feminine-passive psychosexual orientation.
13. Shows heightened ambivalent conflicts.
15. Prefers to express emotion within intellectual framework, rather than directly.
17. Uses inner resources (rather than looking to external environment) to handle anxiety.
25. Has bisexual tendencies.
33. Is prone to depression or mood swings.
34. Ways of emotional expression are flexible and diversified.
50. Desires strong and intimate interpersonal relationships.

Motivational Variables

A. Items achieving a significance level of .02 to .05:

10. Uses parental ideals to set own goals.
5. Strong exhibitionistic needs and desires for recognition are tied in with achievement.
39. Values work primarily as permitting expression of inner personality.
37. Curiosity likely to be a prominent determinant of work.
49. Has a need to integrate internal and external experiences in a comprehensive way.
27. Strong ego-involvement and conflict expressed in work.

B. Items achieving a significance level of .10:

30. Motivated by a desire to master or interpret natural forces or reality.
20. Fears mediocrity in performance.
9. Seems to be strongly self-directed and self-disciplined.

C. Nonsignificant items:

8. Values productive achievement as an end in itself.

22. Value system strongly determined by prevailing cultural standards.

28. Detached from strong desires for direct self-gratification.

35. Works primarily to provide internal satisfactions, with little regard for the product.

36. Has broad time-perspective and strong orientation to the future.

41. Productivity tied up with superego demands.

48. Work is likely to infuse or determine his entire mode of living, rather than being split off.

NOTE: Numbers 10, 12, 19, 22, 40, 42 and 50 were reverse scored.

IV

Items Differentiating Between Artists and Research Scientists According to Major Areas of Variables

Thinking and Perception Variables

A. Items achieving a significance level of .05 or smaller:
   12. Works more originally in somewhat structured, rather than more unstructured situations.
B. Items achieving a significance level of .10:
   29. Shows unusual emphasis on the elaboration of fantasy.
   43. Is responsive to sensory experience data.
   47. Displays novelty in ideational activity.
C. All other items were nonsignificant.

Emotional Variables

A. Items achieving a significance level of .02 or smaller:
   42. Tends to be highly introspective, reflective about sex.

B. Items achieving a significance level of .10:
    31. Can convey experiences or feelings so that another's emotional response is aroused.
    46. Can easily establish a multiplicity of identifications.
C. All other items were nonsignificant.

Motivational Variables

A. No items were significant.

V

Items Differentiating Between Research Scientists and Businessmen According to Major Areas of Variables

Thinking and Perception Variables

A. Items achieving a significance level of .05 or smaller:

21. Seeks to depart radically in his expressions and thinking from the usual, obvious, or hackneyed.

23. Can loosen or relax controls in thinking without personality disorganization.

24. Shows richness in symbolic and descriptive expression and association.

38. Interests point to the theoretical and abstract rather than the practical and realistic.

44. Has capacity for recombining, reorganizing visual conceptions.

47. Displays novelty in ideational activity.

B. Items achieving a significance level of .10:

18. Accepts reality but sees it in a way different from others.
11. Can tolerate ambiguities in the perceptual area.
43. Is responsive to sensory experience data.

C. All other items were nonsignificant.

Emotional Variables

A. Items achieving a significance level of .05 or smaller:

1. Shows a strong tendency for sensuous gratification.
14. Has strong emotional leanings for intellectual activity.
40. Imitates and depends on others in thinking and action (reverse scored).
45. Is challenged by frustration and anxiety-producing situations rather than being overwhelmed by them.

B. Items achieving a significance level of .10:

16. Is sensitive to the moods and feelings of others.
32. Is sensitive to his internal environment, needs, wishes, desires.

C. All other items were nonsignificant.

Motivational Variables

A. Items achieving a significance level of .05 or smaller:

37. Curiosity likely to be a prominent determinant of work.
10. Uses parental ideals to set his own goals (reverse scored).
9. Seems to be strongly self-directed and self-disciplined.
27. Strong ego involvement and conflict expressed in work.
30. Motivated by a desire to master or interpret natural forces or reality.

B. Items achieving a significance level of .10:

39. Values work primarily as permitting expression of inner personality.

C. All other items were nonsignificant.

VI

Personal Data on Subjects[a]

| | | | FAMILY DATA | |
FATHER'S FORMAL EDUCATION	MOTHER'S FORMAL EDUCATION	SUBJECT'S PLACE IN FAMILY[b]	FAMILY'S RESIDENCE: *Rural/Urban*	SOCIOECONOMIC LEVEL *(Estimated from Interview)*
1. Parochial	None	Middle	Rural (Europe)	Middle class
2. Incomplete grammar school	None	Youngest	Urban	Lower
3. Incomplete grammar school	Grammar school	Youngest	Urban	Lower middle
4. Incomplete grammar school	Grammar school	Middle	Rural	Lower middle
5. Parochial	Parochial	Oldest	Semiurban (Europe)	Lower middle

[a] The age of the subject, his scientific field, his father's and mother's occupations, and the number of siblings have been eliminated to maintain the anonymity of the subjects.

[b] Occupations of *brothers,* in order of frequency: business, science, engineering, medicine, law, skilled technical work, art, teaching, military; of *sisters:* housewife, business, teaching, professional work, art, science, nursing, skilled technical work.

FAMILY DATA

FATHER'S FORMAL EDUCATION	MOTHER'S FORMAL EDUCATION	SUBJECT'S PLACE IN FAMILY[b]	FAMILY'S RESIDENCE: *Rural/Urban*	SOCIOECONOMIC LEVEL (*Estimated from Interview*)
6. Grammar school	Grammar school	Youngest	Rural	Lower middle
7. Ph.D.	University	Oldest	Urban-small town	Upper middle
8. Biological father: high school; stepfather: D.D.S.	High school	Only	Rural until 10 years; then urban	Lower middle
9. High school	Incomplete high school	Youngest	Urban	Middle
10. Incomplete grammar school	None	Oldest	Semiurban	Lower
11. L.L.B.	None	Middle	Rural	Lower middle
12. Incomplete grammar school	Incomplete grammar school	Only	Urban	Lower
13. Elementary: European	Elementary: European	Middle	Rural	Lower
14. Incomplete high school	None	Oldest	Urban	Middle
15. Parochial	None	Only	Urban	Lower
16. High school?	Grammar school	Oldest	Urban	Upper
17. Minimum: European	Incomplete grammar school	Oldest	Urban (Europe)	Upper
18. Incomplete grammar school	High school	Oldest	Urban	Lower
19. High school	High school	Oldest	Urban	Upper
20. High school	Incomplete grammar school	Youngest	Urban	Middle
21. High school	Foreign	Oldest	Urban	Lower
22. High school	Incomplete high school	Oldest	Urban	Middle
23. University: European	Foreign	Oldest	Urban (Europe)	Middle
24. Foreign	None	Youngest	Urban	Lower
25. High school	High school	Oldest	Rural-small Western town	Lower

26. Foreign; night school: American	Foreign	Oldest	Urban-small town	Low middle
27. University	University	Middle	Urban	Upper
28. Foreign	Foreign	Youngest	Urban	Middle
29. Incomplete high school	None	Youngest	Urban	Low middle
30. High school	Incomplete high school	Oldest	Urban	Lower
31. D.D.S.	High school	Only	Urban	Low middle
32. High school	High school	Middle	Urban	Low middle
33. Ph. D.	University	Youngest	Urban	Upper
34. Grammar school	None	Only	Urban-small town	Upper
35. High school	Foreign	Oldest	Urban (Europe)	Middle
36. High school	High school	Oldest	Urban-small town	Middle
37. Parochial	None	Oldest	Urban	Lower middle
38. Incomplete university?	High school	Oldest	Urban	Lower
39. Foreign	None	Oldest	Urban	Lower
40. Foreign	None	Middle	Urban	Low middle

PERSONAL DATA ON SUBJECTS

School Achievement Record (Based on subject's report)	Chief Interests in Childhood					
	Sports	Science	Reading	Social	Mechanical	Artistic
1. Good		X	X		X	
2. Excellent (special science high school)	X	X	X			
3. Good	X		X			
4. Good	X		X			
5. Good			X	X		
6. Good	X		X			
7. Good, (poor, early start in school)		X	X			X
8. Good (excellent from later high school years)			X		X	X
9. Fair			X		X	X
10. Excellent	X	X	X			
11. Excellent	X		X		X	X

285

School Achievement Record (Based on subject's report)	Chief Interests in Childhood					
	Sports	Science	Reading	Social	Mechanical	Artistic
12. Good (excellent in science subjects)		X	X			
13. Good	X				X	
14. Excellent		X	X			X
15. Excellent (skipped grades)		X				
16. Excellent (skipped grades—graduated from high school at 14)	X	X				X
17. Good (excellent in math., sciences)	X	X	X			
18. Fair (good in college)	X	X	X			X
19. Good		X	X			X
20. Good	X			X		
21. Excellent	X		X			
22. Good	X	X				
23. Good	X	X	X			
24. Excellent			X		X	X
25. Excellent		X	X			
26. Excellent	X			X		X
27. Excellent	X	X	X		X	
28. Good		X	X			X
29. Excellent (from fifth grade on)		X	X	X		
30. Fair (good only in latter college years			X			
31. Excellent			X			
32. Fair	X		X			
33. Excellent	X	X	X			
34. Excellent		X	X			X
35. Excellent	X		X			
36. Excellent	X	X	X			X
37. Excellent		X	X			
38. Excellent		X	X			X
39. Fair	X					X
40. Fair	X	X	X			X

RATING OF ATTITUDES TOWARDS PARENTS
(Based on interview data)

| + = positive
− = negative
± = ambivalent | | | DESCRIPTIVE CHARACTERISTICS ATTRIBUTED TO FATHER
(Listed in order of frequency) | |
FATHER	MOTHER		Positive	Negative
Subjects				
1. + [1]	+		Admirable human being	Distant, emotionally withdrawn
2. − [6, 9]	−		Self-made success	Too passive, timid
3. ± [6]	−		Socially adept	Unsuccessful in life
4. + [3]	[7]		Great interest in his children	Reserved, too quiet
5. ± [1, 9]	+		Reasonable man, rational, logical	Stern; a hard disciplinarian
6. + [3, 9]	+		Modest, quiet, unassuming	Rigid; unrelenting
7. ± [5]	−		Kindly	Unhappy in marriage
8. + [3, 8, 7]	±		Adheres to tradition	Disordered; alcoholic; gambler
9. ± [6, 9]	[10]		Understanding	Too worried about money
10. − [5, 9]	+		Hard-working	Overly conservative
11. [7]	−		Takes responsibilities seriously	A hated person
12. − [6, 9]	±		Honest	Socially inept
13. + [4]	+		Devout and religious person	Critical
14. + [6]	+		Content and happy man	Unrealistic
15. − [6, 9]	−		Interested in cultural and intellectual things	
16. + [5]	−		Very intelligent, smart	
17. + [1]	+		Valued things other than money	
18. + [6]	−			
19. − [6]	±			
20. ± [5]	−			
21. + [5]	−			
22. ± [5]	− [7]			

[1] European bred, over 40 years of age.
[2] European bred, under 40 years of age.
[3] American, rural, over 40 years of age.
[4] American, rural, under 40 years of age.
[5] American, urban, over 40 years of age.
[6] American, urban, under 40 years of age.
[7] Own parent not well known because of early death, divorce, or work away from home.
[8] Refers to stepfather.
[9] Father living at home but little time spent with son.
[10] Insufficient data to permit rating.

287

RATING OF ATTITUDES TOWARDS PARENTS
(Based on interview data)

+ = positive − = negative ± = ambivalent			DESCRIPTIVE CHARACTERISTICS ATTRIBUTED TO MOTHER (Listed in order of frequency)	
	FATHER	MOTHER	*Positive*	*Negative*
Subjects				
23.	− 1	+	Intelligent; shrewd	Overprotective;
24.	− 5, 7	+	Proud of me, and of all her	possessive
25.	+ 3, 7	−	children	Babyish, imma-
26.	± 6	−	More intimate and closer	ture; hysterical
27.	± 6	+	than father	Distant and unin-
28.	− 6	−	Good, kind, fair	volved
29.	− 6, 9	±	Cultured woman; esthetic in-	Anxious, fearful
30.	± 5	−	terests	Too aggressive;
31.	− 6, 7	±	Serious and hard working	domineering
32.	+ 6, 9	+	woman	Neurotic; odd;
33.	± 5	+	Quick, lively	psychologically
34.	− 6, 9	−	Understanding; maternal;	disturbed
35.	− 2, 7	±	loving	Inadequate mother
36.	− 6	±	Quiet, content	Disliked by all
37.	− 1	−	Happily married	Unhappy, miser-
38.	7	−	Vivacious, humorous	able person
39.	− 6, 9	−	Independent, rebellious,	Overindulgent; un-
40.	− 6, 9	10	"a mind of her own"	self disciplined
			Realistic about money	Overly cautious,
			Decisive	conservative
			Humanitarian values;	Too stern; hard
			worked for good of the	disciplinarian
			community	Rigid
				A nag; a shrew;
				very critical
				Antisocial person-
				ality
				Overly intellectual

[1] European bred, over 40 years of age.
[2] European bred, under 40 years of age.
[3] American, rural, over 40 years of age.
[4] American, rural, under 40 years of age.
[5] American, urban, over 40 years of age.
[6] American, urban, under 40 years of age.
[7] Own parent not well known because of early death, divorce, or work away from home.
[8] Refers to stepfather.
[9] Father living at home but little time spent with son.
[10] Insufficient data to permit rating.

BIBLIOGRAPHY

1. Anderson, H. H. (ed.). *Creativity and Its Cultivation.* New York: Harper, 1959.

2. Ashby, E. *Technology and the Academics.* London: Macmillan, 1958.

3. Barron, F. "Complexity-simplicity as a Personality Dimension." *Journal of Abnormal and Social Psychology, 48:* 170, 1953.

4. Barron, F. "Originality in Relation to Personality and Intellect." *Journal of Personality, 25:* 730, 1957.

5. Barron, F. "Some Correlates of Independence of Judgment." *Journal of Personality, 21:* 287, 1953.

6. Bartlett, F. *Thinking: An Experimental and Social Study.* New York: Basic Books, 1958.

7. Beardslee, D. C., and O'Dowd, D. D. "The College-Student Image of the Scientist." *Science, 133:* 997, 1961.

8. Bellak, L. "Creativity: Some Random Notes to a Systematic Consideration." *Journal of Protective Techniques, 22:* 363, 1958.

9. Bergler, E. *The Writer and Psychoanalysis.* New York: Doubleday, 1950.

289

10. Blatt, S. J., and Stein, M. I. "Some Personality, Value and Cognitive Characteristics of the Creative Person." *American Journal of Psychology, 12:* 406, 1957.

11. Brimhall, D. R. "Family Resemblances among American Men of Science." *American Naturalist, 56:* 504, 1922; *57:* 74, 137, 326, 1923.

12. Brozek, J. "The Age Problem in Research Workers: Psychological Viewpoint." *Scientific Monthly, 72:* 355, 1951.

13. Cannon, W. B. "The Role of Chance in Discovery." *Scientific Monthly, 50:* 204, 1940.

14. Cattell, J. Mck. "A Statistical Study of American Men of Science: The Selection of a Group of One Thousand Scientific Men." *Science,* New Series, *24:* 658–65, 669–707, 732–42 (1906); also *32:* 633–48, 672–88, 1910.

15. Cattell, R. B., and Drevdahl, J. E. "A Comparison of the Personality Profile (16 P. F.) of Eminent Researchers with That of Eminent Teachers and Administrators and of the General Population." *British Journal of Psychology, 46:* 248, 1955.

16. *Creativity as a Process.* Report of a Conference held at Arden House, Harriman, N.Y., October 10–12, 1956.

17. Dennis, W. "Age and Productivity among Scientists." *Science, 123:* 724, 1956.

18. Dennis, W. "The Age Decrement in Outstanding Scientific Contributions: Fact or Artifact?" *American Psychologist, 13:* 457, 1958.

19. Drevdahl, J. E. "Factors of Importance for Creativity." *Journal of Clinical Psychology, 12:* 21, 1956.

20. Dubos, R. "Scientist and Public." *Science, 33:* 1207, 1961.

21. Eiduson, Bernice T. "Artist and Non-Artist: A Comparative Psychological Study." *Journal of Personality, 26:* 13, 1958.

22. Eiduson, Bernice T. "Artist and Research Scientist: A Comparative Study." *Proceedings,* American Psychological Association, Washington, D.C., September, 1958.

23. Eiduson, Bernice T. "The Changing Self-Images of Research Scientists." *Proceedings,* American Psychological Association, Cincinnati, September 1959.

24. Federn, P. *Ego Psychology and the Psychoses.* New York: Basic Books, 1952.

25. Frenkel-Brunswik, Else. "Intolerance of Ambiguity as

an Emotional and Perceptual Personality Variable." *Journal of Personality, 18:* 108, 1949.

26. Freud, S. "Dostoevski and Parricide." In F. Dostoevski, *Stavrogin's Confession,* New York: Lear, 1947.

27. Freud, S. *A General Introduction to Psychoanalysis.* New York: Boni, Liveright, 1920.

28. Galton, F. *Hereditary Genius.* New York: D. Appleton, 1870.

29. Ghiselin, B. *The Creative Process.* Los Angeles: University of California Press, 1952.

30. Glass, B. "The Academic Scientist, 1940–1960." *Science, 132:* 598, 1960.

31. Gough, H. G. "Stylistic Variations in the Self-Views and Work Attitudes of a Sample of Professional Research Scientists." *Proceedings,* Western Psychological Association, Monterey, California, April 1958.

32. Guilford, J. P. "Creativity." *American Psychologist, 5:* 444, 1950.

33. Guilford J. P., Christensen, P. R., Frick, J. W., and Merrifield, P. R. "The Relations of Creative-Thinking Aptitudes to Non-Aptitude Personality Traits." *Reports from the Psychological Laboratory,* University of Southern California, No. 20, December 1957.

34. Guilford, J. P., Keltner, N. W., and Christensen, P. R. "A Factor-Analytic Study Across the Domains of Learning, Creativity and Evaluations: I. Hypotheses and Description of Tests." *Reports from The Psychological Laboratory,* University of Southern California, No. 11, July 1954.

35. Hall, W. B. "The Development of a Technique for Assessing Esthetic Predispositions and the Application to a Sample of Professional Research Scientists." *Proceedings,* Western Psychological Association, Monterey, California, April 1958.

36. Hardy, G. H. *A Mathematician's Apology.* New York: Cambridge University Press, 1941.

37. Harms, E. (ed.). *Fundamentals of Psychology: The Psychology of Thinking.* New York: Annals of the New York Academy of Sciences, Vol. 91, 1960.

38. Hart, H. H. "The Integrative Factor in Creativity." *Psychiatric Quarterly, 24:* 1, 1950.

39. Hebb, D. O. "Problems Relating to Thought." In D. O. Hebb, *A Textbook of Psychology.* Philadelphia: W. B. Saunders, 1958.

40. Henry, W. E. "The Business Executive: The Psycho-dynamics of a Social Role." *American Journal of Sociology, 54:* 286, 1949.

41. Holton, G. "Modern Science and the Intellectual Tradition." *Science, 131:* 1187, 1960.

42. Hulbeck, C. R. "Psychoanalytical Thoughts in Creativity." *American Journal of Psychoanalysis, 13:* 84, 1953.

43. Kelly, G. A. *The Psychology of Personal Constructs.* New York: Norton, 1955, Vol. I.

44. Knapp, R. H., and Goodrich, H. B. *Origins of American Scientists.* Chicago: University of Chicago Press, 1952.

45. Knapp, R. H., and Greenbaum, J. J. *The Younger American Scholar: His Collegiate Origins.* Chicago: University of Chicago Press, 1953.

46. Kris, E. "On Preconscious Mental Processes." In D. Rapaport (ed.), *Organization and Pathology of Thought.* New York: Columbia University Press, 1951.

47. Kris, E. *Psychoanalytic Explorations in Art.* New York: International Universities Press, 1952.

48. Kubie, L. S. *Neurotic Distortion of the Creative Process.* Lawrence, Kansas: University of Kansas Press, 1958.

49. Kubie, L. S. "Some Unsolved Problems of the Scientific Career." *American Scientist, 41:* 596, 1953; *42:* 104, 1954.

50. Lee, H. B. "A Theory Concerning Free Creation in the Inventive Arts." *Psychiatry 3:* 229, 1940.

51. Lehman, H. C. *Age and Achievement.* Princeton, N.J.: Princeton University Press, 1953.

52. Lehman, H. C. "The Chemist's Most Creative Years." *Science, 127:* 1213, 1958.

53. Lehman, H. C. "Men's Creative Production Rate." *Scientific Monthly, 78:* 321, 1954.

54. Leuba, C. "A New Look at the Beginnings of Curiosity and Creativity." *Proceedings,* Ohio State University Conference on Creativity, Granville, Ohio, 1952.

55. Lorand, S. "A Note on the Psychology of the Inventor." *Psychoanalytic Quarterly, 3:* 30, 1934.

56. Lowenfeld, V. *The Nature of Creative Activity.* New York: Harcourt, Brace, 1939.

57. McCarthy, Mary, "Characters in Fiction." *Partisan Review 28:* 171, 1961.

58. McClelland, D. C., Baldwin, A. L., Bronfenbrenner,

U., and Strodtbeck, F. L. *Talent and Society.* Princeton, N.J.: Van Nostrand, 1958.

59. McKellar, P. *Imagination and Thinking: A Psychological Analysis.* New York: Basic Books, 1957.

60. Mead, Margaret, and Metraux, Rhoda. "Image of the Scientists among High School Students." *Science, 126:* 384, 1957.

61. Meer, B., and Stein, M. I. "Measures of Intelligence and Creativity." *Journal of Psychology, 39:* 117, 1955.

62. Michael, D. N. "Scientist through Adolescent Eyes: What We Need to Know, Why We Need to Know it." *Scientific Monthly, 84:* 135, 1957.

63. Montmasson, J. M. *Invention and the Unconscious.* London: Kegan, Paul, Trench, Trubner, 1931.

64. Murphy, G. *Human Potentialities.* New York: Basic Books, 1958.

65. Patrick, Catherine. "How Creative Thought Is Related to Thinking." *American Psychologist, 4:* 266, 1949.

66. Patrick, Catherine, "Scientific Thought." *Journal of Psychology, V:* 55, 1938.

67. Rank, O. *Art and Artists.* New York: Knopf, 1932.

68. Redlich, F. "The Psychiatrist in Caricature: An Analysis of Unconscious Attitudes toward Psychiatry." *American Journal of Orthopsychiatry, 20:* 560, 1950.

69. Roe, Anne. "Alcohol and Creative Work: Part I—Painters." *Quarterly Journal of Studies in Alcohol, 6:* 415, 1946.

70. Roe, Anne. "Analysis of Group Rorschachs of Biologists." *Rorschach Research Exchange, 13:* 25, 1949.

71. Roe, Anne. "Artists and Their Work." *Journal of Personality, 15:* 1, 1946.

72. Roe, Anne. "Group Rorschachs of Physical Scientists." *Journal of Projective Techniques, 14:* 385, 1950.

73. Roe, Anne. *The Making of a Scientist.* New York: Dodd, Mead, 1952.

74. Roe, Anne. "Personality and Vocation." *Transactions of the New York Academy of Sciences, 9:* 257, 1947.

75. Roe, Anne. "A Psychological Study of Eminent Biologists." *Psychological Monographs, 65* (No. 14): 68, 1951.

76. Roe, Anne. "A Psychological Study of Eminent Psychologists and Anthropologists, and a Comparison with Biological and Physical Scientists." *Psychological Monographs, 67:* (No. 2) 55, 1953.

293

77. Roe, Anne. *The Psychology of Occupations,* New York: Wiley, 1956.

78. Roe, Anne. "A Study of Imagery in Research Scientists." *Journal of Personality, 19:* 459, 1951.

79. Rogers, C. R. "Toward a Theory of Creativity." *ETC: A Review of General Semantics, 11:* 249, 1953.

80. Sachs, H. *The Creative Unconscious.* Cambridge: Sci-Art Publishers, 1942.

81. Sayre, W. S. "Scientists and American Science Policy." *Science, 133:* 859, 1961.

82. Schneider, D. S. *The Psychoanalyst and the Artist.* New York: Farrar, Straus, 1950.

83. Sharpe, Ella. "Similar and Divergent Unconscious Determinants Underlying the Sublimations of Pure Art and Pure Science." *International Journal of Psychoanalysis, 16:* 186, 1935.

84. Smith, P. (ed.). *Creativity: An Examination of the Creative Process.* New York: Hastings House, 1959.

85. Snow, C. P. *The Two Cultures and the Scientific Revolution.* Cambridge: Cambridge University Press, 1959.

86. Spearman, C. *Creative Mind.* London: Nisbet, 1931.

87. Stein, M. I. "Creativity and Culture." *Journal of Psychology, 36:* 311, 1953.

88. Stein, M. I. "Creativity and the Scientist," in The National Physical Laboratories, *The Direction of Research Establishments,* No. 3, London, 1957, pp. 1–19.

89. Stein, M. I., Mackenzie, J. M., *et al.* "A Case Study of a Scientist." in H. Burton and R. E. Harris (eds.), *Case History in Clinical and Abnormal Psychology.* New York: Harper, 1955, Vol. 2.

90. Stein, M. I., and Meer, B. "Perceptual Organization in a Study of Creativity." *Journal of Psychology, 37:* 39, 1954.

91. Stern, G. G., Stein, M. I., and Bloom, B. S. *Methods in Personality Assessment.* Glencoe, Ill.: Free Press, 1956.

92. Taylor, C. W. (ed.). *The 1955 University of Utah Research Conference in the Identification of Creative Scientific Talent.* Salt Lake City: University of Utah Press, 1956.

93. Taylor, C. W. (ed.). *The Second (1957) Research Conference on the Identification of Creative Scientific Talent.* Salt Lake City: University of Utah Press, 1957.

94. Terman, L. M. "The Discovery and Encouragement of Exceptional Talent." *American Psychologist, 9:* 221, 1954.

95. Terman, L. M., *et al. Genetic Studies of Genius.* Stanford: Stanford University Press, 1925–1947, Vols. I–IV.

96. Terman, L. M. "Scientists and Nonscientists in a Group of 800 Gifted Men." *Psychological Monographs, 68:* 44, 1954.

97. Trilling, L. *A Gathering of Fugitives.* Boston: Beacon Press, 1956.

98. Tumin, M. "Obstacles to Creativity." *ETC: A Review of General Semantics, 11:* 261, 1953.

99. Van Zelst, R. H., and Kerr, W. A. "Some Correlates of Technical and Scientific Productivity." *Journal of Abnormal and Social Psychology, 46:* 470, 1951.

100. Vernon, M. D. "The Relationship of Occupation to Personality." *British Journal of Psychology, 31:* 294, 1941.

101. Vinacke, W. E. "Creative Thinking." In *The Psychology of Thinking.* New York: McGraw-Hill, 1952.

102. Visher, S. S. *Scientists Starred 1903–43 in "American Men of Science": A Study of Collegiate and Doctoral Training, Birthplace, Distribution, Backgrounds, and Developmental Influences.* Baltimore: Johns Hopkins University Press, 1947.

103. Welch, L. "Recombination of Ideas in Creative Thinking." *Journal of Applied Psychology, 30:* 638, 1946.

104. Wilson, R. C., Guilford, J. P., *et al.* "A Factor-analytic Study of Creative Thinking Abilities." *Psychometrika, 19:* 297, 1954.

105. Wilson, R. C., Guilford, J. P., *et al.* "The Measurement of Individual Differences in Originality." *Psychological Bulletin, 50:* 362, 1953.

106. Woodworth, D. G. "A Fictional Study of Trait Rankings Used in an Assessment of Professional Research Scientists." *Proceedings,* Western Psychological Association, Monterey, California, April 1958.

INDEX